Policy-Making and Planning
in the Health Sector

Policy-Making and Planning in the Health Sector

**KENNETH LEE
and ANNE MILLS**

CROOM HELM
London & Sydney

© 1982 Kenneth Lee and Anne Mills
Reprinted 1985

Croom Helm Ltd, Provident House, Burrell Row,
Beckenham, Kent BR3 1AT

Croom Helm Australia Pty Ltd, Suite 4, 6th Floor,
64-76 Kippax Street, Surry Hills, NSW 2010, Australia

British Library Cataloguing in Publication Data

Lee, Kenneth
    Policy-making and planning in the health sector.
    1. Health services administration—Great Britain—Decision
    making.
I. Title   II. Mills, Anne
362.1'068   RA395.G6

ISBN 0-85664-965-1
ISBN 0-7099-4111-0 (Pbk)

Printed and bound in Great Britain by
Biddles Ltd, Guildford and King's Lynn

CONTENTS

FIGURES

TO CAROLINE AND PATRICK

PREFACE

From 1976 to 1979, the authors worked closely together on the evaluation of strategic and operational planning in the National Health Service, as members of a multidisciplinary team with various academic skills, and training and experience obtained largely in the health sector. The opportunity for the research was provided by the introduction of a formal planning system into the NHS, and the study was funded by the Department of Health and Social Security (DHSS) to monitor and interpret the policy-making and planning processes of a number of health agencies. Its ultimate aim was to generate recommendations to the DHSS on the extent to which the structure and processes of NHS planning might further be developed and improved.

The research was completed at the end of 1979 and, although this text goes well beyond the remit of the original research, it has drawn considerably on the empirical material produced during the course of that study. Indeed, that research provided the springboard for the more general consideration of major issues in policy-making and planning now presented in this book.

There are, of course, dangers in suggesting that one can extrapolate from any country's experience, given the all-too-noticeable differences in the cultural, social, political and economic backgrounds of the various health care systems that exist throughout the world. None the less, while the circumstances of the health sector and the relationships within it will vary from country to country, all countries attempting to develop their health sector in a systematic fashion will face problems of rationing resources, determining the appropriate level - central, regional or local - for planning activities, setting up an appropriate control system, and developing inter-sectoral links across organisational boundaries. Accordingly, with a general and international audience of practitioners, academics and students very much in mind, this book aims to present a relatively non-technical analysis of the various concepts and methods surrounding health policy analysis and planning, which none the less makes demands on the reader to come to terms with the complex issues that presently face the health sector.

ACKNOWLEDGEMENTS

We are especially indebted to the many members, officers and staff of the various health authorities in England with whom we were in regular contact during the course of our research work. We were given far more assistance than we had any right to expect, and our questions were greeted with unfailing courtesy. To the many people who gave generously of their time and thought we would like to express our appreciation.

We are deeply indebted to our former colleagues on the research team, Keith Barnard and Joy Reynolds. Our research project was very much a team effort and we owe much to them both, not only in their contribution to the analysis of NHS planning, but also in the stimulus they gave us to look more deeply into policy-making and planning in general. We would also like to acknowledge the assistance of many of our colleagues, past and present, at the Nuffield Centre in Leeds. In particular, we wish to record our appreciation to Jack Hallas, Chris Ham, Andrew Long, Tom Rathwell and David Towell, who helped us to formulate our ideas and at various stages commented upon one or more of our draft chapters. Without the help of all these people, the book would have contained far more errors than it does; for all that remain, the responsibility is entirely ours.

Finally, we reserve our special gratitude for Miss Jane Thompson for her administrative efficiency and secretarial skill in preparing the entire manuscript for publication.

Kenneth Lee and Anne Mills

1 INTRODUCTION

In modern times, health services have shown themselves only too capable of absorbing a large share of the resources that nations have available for public and private expenditure. In the developed world, it has proved possible until recently to finance the growth in health services from national economic growth. Now, however, as nations are faced with problems of slow or negative economic growth, government health policies are increasingly directed towards setting limits on the resources absorbed by the health sector. In many developing countries, rather different concerns result from the ever-present context of tight financial constraints. Third World governments seek to extend basic health care to their entire populations at a cost both the state and individuals can afford. The common factor, in both developing and developed countries, is that the scale of health expenditure is determined to a significant extent by the management of the economy and by its performance, which either enable or limit the scope and fulfilment of health policies.

In the burgeoning literature on health policy, two underlying policy objectives are apparent to justify increased public expenditure on health-related services: first, in terms of improving access to, and use of, such services for under--served or deprived groups in the population; and, second, in terms of improving the well-being of the whole population. The consequence of this first policy objective, namely determining who will receive health care and, hence, whose needs will be deferred or denied, has turned out to be perhaps the most controversial function that the health sector performs. Nor are there easy answers to the second policy objective, for it is increasingly recognised that health is a product of a number of factors of which the availability and consumption of health services constitutes only one. There is no easy way of discerning, still less of proving, any clear causal links between levels of health care expenditure and states of health. It needs to be accepted, therefore, that health care expenditure must compete with other claimants on the public and private purse which contribute to the population's well-being. Moreover, the improvement of health is unlikely to be an overriding priority for any government or individual, and the demand for resources to improve health will be weighed against other expenditures which satisfy quite different objectives.

The boundary between public and private provision of

welfare services is located differently in different countries and, subject both to political swings and financial expediency, will vary over time. The polar extremes of total 'free enterprise' and total 'socialised medicine' - the one with no government and tax finance and the other with no private sector - are uncommon, even as ideals. This line of argument does not of course deny that, for instance, the British and American systems of health care represent quite different approaches to the financing and delivery of health care, with implications for efficiency, cost containment and equity. Yet virtually all countries have significant government involvement in the health sector and, almost irrespective of the type of health system, are faced with the fundamental issues of establishing and attaining priorities and influencing the distribution of resources. In essence, planning addresses itself to this task of relating the spending plans of various health agencies to the aims of policy, and then of influencing future expenditure in the desired direction.

But planning has not always enjoyed universal acceptance. Planning could be said to convey a sense of conscious effort to choose a desired future, and in that sense has always been practised, whether or not through a formal planning system. Whether, however, people are happy to be called planners when they engage in such an activity depends on what they understand 'planning' to mean, for understanding of this term has changed over time. Going back thirty years or more in the UK would bring to mind a view which saw planning as imposed 'rationality'. This view, the aftermath of wartime restrictions and controls, meant that planning for some time did not enjoy uncritical acceptance. However, by the 1960s the prevailing ideology favoured the purposeful shaping of the social welfare system and intervention in the market-place. In both the US and the UK, it led to a strong tide in favour of amalgamation, co-ordination and integration - to create larger and more comprehensive institutions, such as big hospitals and area--based organisational structures, to facilitate growth, improve efficiency and reap economies of scale.

Despite increasing levels of conflict between different social groups, which produced demands for both staff and community participation, the emphasis of public policy continued to be on improved organisation, better use of resources and more comprehensive planning designed to ensure that services were developed and provided according to 'community' needs. Turning, however, to the present day it is apparent that the term 'planning' has lost much of its cachet when compared to the importance attached to it in the 1960s and early 1970s. In the United States, the Health Policy and Resources Development Act of 1974 was designed to match the expansionary optimism of the 1960s with the cost-containment mentality of the 1970s by creating a national network of state and local health planning agencies. Although there was still general concern about the need to improve the overall health of the population, cost containment increasingly took the front seat in planning efforts. In other words, the prime concern of planning has become regulation of the existing health sector rather than developing innovative services for the future. Likewise, in the UK, the reorganisation of the NHS in 1974 brought with it a belief that the new NHS planning system would be the cornerstone of management and purposeful change in the health service. Today, planning is taking a back seat in government pronouncements and alternative approaches, such as local autonomy, cash limits and private health insurance, are in vogue.

And yet, the problems remain: even if the term 'planning' is no longer fashionable, it is inevitable that some decisions have to be taken somewhere, by someone, on the levels of service provision, and on the priorities for distributing resources both geographically and between different groups in the population. Indeed, it can be argued that these decisions are more important in times of economic stringency and austerity.

The late 1970s and early 1980s, therefore, mark a change in the context of planning in a number of developed countries. Now, planners are faced, and are likely to continue to be faced for some time, with planning for economies, cost containment and the 'rationalisation' or closure of health facilities, rather than for growth. Such a financial climate will increase conflict within the health system. No longer can everyone reap the fruits of growth: instead, some must lose if others are to gain. Hence it is crucial that planners anticipate the interests and commitments of affected groups, and build political support for their proposals, in addition to producing technically sound reports. Through such behaviour, planners might thereby minimise the gap - frequently encountered - between planning and implementation.

It is against such a changing backcloth that this book has been produced. Its aim is to explore the tasks and inherent problems that countries face in attempting to improve the health and well-being of their communities through conscious and deliberate attempts to develop policies and implement plans for the development of health-related services. However, the purpose is not to produce a 'how to do it' treatise: such textbooks exist already. Instead, the emphasis of the book is on identifying the conditions that have to be satisfied for effective policy-making and planning, in order to offer a critique of the modes of behaviour that appear to be conducive to the acceptability and success of planning. The authors intend that the book should raise issues that are relevant to those political contexts where the systematic development of health policies is being actively pursued or contemplated.

Accordingly, the next chapter (Chapter 2 - 'The Study of Policy-making and Planning in the Health Sector') tackles the clarification of the various terms associated with policy-making and planning, in order to define these terms within the context of the health sector. First, however, consideration is given to health and to the health sector itself. The convenient assumption that medicine equals health, and more medicine equals better health, has been strongly contested in recent times. In consequence, it has become more generally recognised that changes in the health and well-being of the population will not necessarily emanate from the medical sector itself.

Many health policy-makers and planners are alive to these truths, but may question whether change is possible and whether corrective action can be taken. Certainly, the health planning perspective does hold that it is possible to plan and co-ordinate the future development of the health care delivery system. However, while some participants may see planning in such terms, others may see it primarily as a means of using social and political influence to cope with conflicting demands. By reviewing recent developments in health planning, especially in the United States and the United Kingdom, Chapter 2 concludes that a credibility gap of some magnitude exists between the rhetoric of comprehensive planning and the reality of health policy-making and planning in many societies today.

In an attempt to explain why such a 'gap' exists, Chapter 3 ('Theories of Health Planning') offers a survey of the various theories of planning behaviour that might be advanced for the health sector. Where attempts have been made to determine how health policies should be developed, and the methods or strategies by which changes should take place, attitudes to planning fall into a number of distinct schools, each of which reflects a particular philosophy and definition of planning.

Hence, before any assessment can be made of the successes or failures of health planning in any one country, it is appropriate to review the assumptions and the features of the various health planning models. Accordingly, Chapter 3 considers the three main schools of thought: the rationalists, the incrementalists and the mixed scanners. These three main approaches can be considered to categorise policy-making and planning along a continuum, the extremities of which are marked by notions of 'incrementalism' and of 'rationalism'. In practice, it is probable that observed instances of planning will always fall somewhere between these two extremes.

Finally, the chapter considers the different circumstances under which planning practice will move towards rationalism or towards incrementalist behaviour. A major, if not necessarily the most important, factor influencing the viability of rational comprehensive planning appears to be the practicality or feasibility of reconciling conflicting goals, values and interests. How much emphasis, then, should be given in planning systems to devising an appropriate process or means of arriving at decisions, and how much to producing a desirable outcome to planning?

The whole issue of the nature of decision-making is taken up in Chapter 4 ('Policy and Decision-making in the Health Sector'). There is little agreement - even at an empirical level - about such crucial questions as who makes the resource allocation decisions in health care, what the objectives of the decision-makers are, and what type of model is most appropriate for the study of health policy-making and implementation. In response, this chapter offers a survey of the literature on individual and corporate objectives, and investigates possible motives for observed behaviour in the health sector.

Fortunately, there is an extensive literature devoted to various managerial and behavioural theories of the firm, though few attempts have been made to relate these to the health sector. Before considering which set of theories might most comfortably fit the reality of health care decision-making, their main details and differences are identified. Managerial theories build up the objectives of the firm by a consideration of the 'utility maximising' behaviour of the key individuals within the firm, whereas behavioural theories relax this maximisation hypothesis and replace it with the concept of 'satisficing'.

It is then argued that private firms and health agencies do possess some features in common, not least in the degree of imprecision about the aims of their respective organisations. This permits a degree of latitude of interpretation to the various actors involved in decision-making, be they politicians, public officials, employees or consumers. It is important, therefore, to clarify the objectives of these various actors if attempts are to be made to reconcile their differences in the wider interests of the whole organisation.

Chapter 5 ('Plans, Programmes and Budgets') shifts the focus of the book towards the framework for planning and explores the nature of the link between the processes of planning and budgeting. The importance of studying the framework for structuring any debate about health sector development can be simply stated: it is this framework that will affect the range of policy options considered and, ultimately, the content and quality of the decisions made. Although planning terminology has changed over the years, there has been a continuing interest in forging a closer and more explicit link between planning and budgeting. PPBS and programme budgeting were developed with this in mind, as well as to introduce economic concepts of efficiency into planning, through analysing the use of resources by the various purposes they served and the results they achieved.

Programme budgeting encounters many methodological difficulties including those of defining and costing programmes, measuring benefits and comparing the costs and benefits of particular projects. None the less, the notion of programme budgeting survives, though in a variety of forms. Enthusiasm has waned in the United States, but a programme budget for health services in the United Kingdom is maintained, and the World Health Organization incorporates a form of programme budgeting in its planning methodology.

Yet, as the chapter goes on to discuss, the organisational issues affecting the operation of programme budgeting are as important as the technical issues. In particular, there is the question of whether, and under what circumstances, policy--makers and planners are inclined, obliged or encouraged to plan and make decisions in terms of programmes and use programme budgets as analytical tools. American experience indicates that the acceptance of PPBS by interested parties, and in particular by those controlling the budgeting process, is crucial to its success. In Britain, the use of a programme budget to frame priorities and guidance for peripheral health agencies has raised comparable issues of its acceptability to local decision-makers, and the extent to which it can be used as both an analytical aid and tool for control.

This issue of control is central to the consideration of health policy and planning, for many governments intervene in the health sector, either to provide services directly as in the UK and in a number of eastern European countries, or indirectly, as in North America and many western European countries. Yet, as is apparent from the discussion in Chapter 6 ('Relationships between Central Government and Peripheral Health Agencies'), government intervention raises the contentious issue of the appropriate level and form of control. Should control be centralised, a national government organising and managing health services directly? Or should some form of decentralised, or even devolved, management be introduced? The chapter considers these questions in terms of the way in which planning systems can and have been used to link central and peripheral health agencies.

Since the controls operated via a health planning system cannot be taken in isolation, the chapter first considers the various mechanisms of influence and control available to central governments. It then looks in detail at the factors influencing the balance of power between centre and periphery in the UK, and at how the UK has attempted to resolve the problems of managing and planning a publicly provided and funded health service, keeping some central authority while permitting local discretion. The chapter concludes by considering how success-ful the UK has been, and how much discretion is maintained by local health agencies. What emerges with force is that a seemingly 'well designed' central policy - even when matched by resources - is not sufficient to ensure implementation if it challenges the motivations and inclinations of those who must carry it out locally.

Chapter 7 ('Local Interest Groups and the Planning Pro-cess') explores this issue further by concentrating on the involvement of different groups in the policy-making and planning process at local level. As it is often far from clear what is meant by such terms as 'participation' and 'consultation', the chapter first looks at the reasons why certain groups have been assigned a legitimate place in the decision-making process, and why others have been denied that 'right'. It then considers whether such terms as participation, consultation and negotiation are concerned directly with the degree of influence upon decision-making, or whether they are merely, and rather loosely, used as terms for different types of participation. It is argued that the former is the appropriate interpretation and that the study of interest group involvement necessitates identifying and exploring who has power to influence decisions, and whose interests are taken into account in the determination of policy and the formulation of plans.

Chapter 7 uses the UK as an example of the ways in which interest groups (such as professional bodies and consumer groups) can be, and are, involved in health planning. It considers what factors might influence the degree of power each group can wield and concludes that if it is, in fact, desirable to encourage the involvement of various groups in health planning, a formal planning system assumes importance not least because it formalises the opportunity for all groups to articulate their views. That apart, the lesson to be learnt is that the involvement in planning of numerous interests, each with their own goals to achieve, can make it difficult for planners to maintain the viability of the planning process, and demands that managers develop political skills to negotiate agreements between interested parties.

The penultimate chapter (Chapter 8 - 'Organisational Linkages in Planning for Health') takes the issue of goal conflict a step further by considering the linkages that are encouraged between public, private and voluntary organisations, both within and outside the health sector, to ensure that each takes into account the impact that their respective policies and activities have upon the health and well-being of the population. Linkages between agencies involved in health-affecting activities can be classified in terms of levels of decision, such as day-to-day activities, short-term planning or long-term strategies. At each of these levels, the degree of co-ordination and collaboration can be hampered or enhanced by a number of factors such as each organisation's own set of loyalties, legal obligations and responsibilities, management procedures and professional affiliations.

How then can co-ordination and linkages over planning and policy issues be encouraged? What structures and processes are most useful? These questions are addressed in Chapter 8, first from a theoretical standpoint and then in terms of a case study of co-ordination between health and related social services in Britain. What is clear from this analysis is that common goals cannot necessarily be assumed to exist between organisations, though common action can be negotiated. Structural arrangements for 'collaboration' cannot, of themselves, guarantee linkages, but they do at least provide means whereby staffs of different agencies can exchange ideas and experiences. However, informal linkages organised by people with appropriate skills and commitment are likely to be an important condition for successful co-ordination between organisations.

Chapter 9 ('Health Planning Systems: Implementation and Evaluation') provides a general overview of the 'outcomes' of policy-making and planning. The chapter stresses that outcomes occur at different levels and stages, in both the formulation of policy and the production of plans. Indeed, the production of a plan can, in one sense, be regarded as an outcome of the planning process. Yet the logic of planning should carry the conviction that the plan will be implemented and that, once implemented, it will have the intended beneficial impact on the health status of the target population. The chapter incorporates an assessment of the impact of the formal health planning system adopted in the UK. This system is analysed in terms of the extent to which the practice and outcomes of planning match up to the objectives of the system. This study makes clear that, however sophisticated the planning methodology, the results have to be acceptable to those upon whom implementation depends. In other words, the 'act' of planning does not, of itself, guarantee a defined future; at best, it is only a way of exploring the possibility of one. In the last analysis, how that exploration is conducted depends crucially upon the varied interests of the organisations, groups and individuals involved.

Hence, it can be concluded that any planning process must be able to cope with conflicting pressures through providing means by which conflicts of interest and values can be reconciled or accommodated in policy- and decision-making. How these pressures and conflicts manifest themselves in the health sector and might best be handled are the recurring themes of this book. By careful analysis in the chapters that follow, it is hoped both to moderate the unduly optimistic expectations often entertained of any planning and policy-making process, and yet point to feasible improvements that could be made to the process of decision-making.

2 THE STUDY OF POLICY-MAKING AND PLANNING IN THE HEALTH SECTOR

1 INTRODUCTION: POLICY AND PLANNING

Before considering the detailed features of policy-making and planning in the health sector in subsequent chapters, it is important first to establish a common understanding, in the context of this book, of the various phenomena associated with 'planning' and 'policy-making'. The vocabulary is less stable than that of the natural sciences, and the field has acquired a terminology which necessitates clarification.

The basic concern of this chapter is the whole subject of the policy-making and planning process in the health sector: from the development of ideas to the formulation of policy; the transformation of policy into a set of objectives; the conversion of objectives into plans through the process of planning; and the translation of plans into a sequence of commitments and actions leading to implementation of the desired changes and, ultimately, an impact on the organisation or its environment. In short, this chapter is primarily aimed at exploring the meaning of these various terms, and placing them in the context of the health sector.

Planning is increasingly regarded as one element of management: indeed, management is sometimes used as a synonym for planning. None the less, for the purposes of this and subsequent chapters, it has proved helpful to draw a practical distinction between planning and management which depends essentially on differentiating the time frame appropriate for each activity. Management is defined as covering day-to-day issues; planning covers issues stretching further into the future. Of course, any one issue is likely to carry both management and planning implications: management and planning are not entirely discrete activities, and both may be undertaken by the same person. However, the utility of such a distinction is indicated by the commonly advanced hypothesis that the pressure of managing day-to-day affairs precludes consideration of longer-term issues: in effect, the demands of the urgent drive out those of the important. A formal planning system is often introduced precisely to ensure that this deflection does not happen.

During the last twenty years or so, in the UK, North America and elsewhere, considerable emphasis has been placed upon experimentation and innovation in health policy. Though seen as mere 'window-dressing' by some commentators, others perceive it as indicative of a disaffection with existing modes of provision and a desire for greater 'rationality' in decision-making. At the same time, there has been increasing emphasis in the health sector, and in government itself, upon accountability, efficiency and effectiveness. These concerns have resulted in a number of innovations centred on encouraging corporate and comprehensive approaches to planning and policy-making. Many of their origins can be traced to the United States and to the development of PPBS, a systems approach that has been espoused by many governments since the mid-1960s.

The desire to 'systematise' the future was, with hindsight, a challenging task. Divergent views can be, and are, held both between and within countries on what the short- and long-term future of health systems should be. The existence of divergent views is given added significance when the task of implementing changes is considered. The larger and more complex the health sector, the greater the potential 'gap' will be between the enunciation of formal policy and whatever is implemented 'on the ground'. Different actors will bring different values and experiences to bear, and respond to different influences and pressures. Yet the implementation stage is crucial because it is the phase whereby 'policy' is shaped into action. Indeed, those responsible for implementation are as much policy-makers as those whose formal roles will have been enacted at earlier stages: the actual impact of policy depends on them.

2 THE HEALTH SECTOR: AN OVERVIEW

Health policy-making and planning cannot be explored without first considering 'health' and the boundaries of the health sector. The debate on 'what is health' appears unending; can it be expressed positively, as 'health is ...', or only negatively, as 'the absence of disease, infirmity, handicap or distress'? The concept of health is elusive, and hope of a practical definition to suit all circumstances illusory. The topic can most easily be explored by considering the absence of health, that is the extent of ill health, its causes and possible remedies, and their implications for health policy and planning.

It is perhaps unnecessary to state that health conditions do vary greatly from country to country and between groups within countries. Clearly, health conditions are significantly worse in the developing world than in more affluent countries, while developing countries have fewer resources to devote to the improvement of health. For instance, it is reported that more than half the population of the world does not have the benefit of adequate health care[1], and that nearly one thousand million people are trapped in a seemingly unending circle of poverty, malnutrition, disease and despair. In the poorest regions of low-income countries, half of all children die during the first year of life. For those who survive beyond the age of five, life expectation is six to eight years less than in developed countries. Expressed in other terms, it is estimated that one-tenth of the life of the average person in a developing country is seriously disrupted by ill health.[2]

What, then, is health for all?[3] According to the World Health Organization, it is to bring within reach of everyone a state of health that enables a person to lead a socially and economically productive life. This transformation cannot be achieved by health services alone, though they can make a major contribution. Moreover, planners and policy-makers are increasingly recognising that substantial improvements in health can be attained without the use of high-technology medical care and highly educated medical manpower. Rather, it is clear that what the rural (and often urban) peoples of the developing world need most to improve their health are more food, better balanced diets, immunisation, safe water supplies, efficient disposal of human waste and family planning services.[4] Such health development can both contribute to, as well as result from, general social and economic development. Accordingly, health development cannot be considered in isolation from general development policy.

This concern about the appropriate role for health services and the limitations of 'orthodox' medical services is not confined to the developing world. The assumption that medicine equals health, and more medicine equals better health, has been strongly contested in recent times in developed countries. As medical services have absorbed more and more resources, the belief that a finite quantity of 'need' would systematically be reduced by efficient and effective medical services has appeared unfounded. Instead, there is the prospect of an 'infinite demand', whether stemming from patients or providers, for increasingly sophisticated and hence expensive equipment and manpower.

As long as consumers were led to expect, and government and providers were prepared to supply, the latest medical treatments, the impact of such treatments upon health itself was very much a secondary consideration. These attitudes are now being changed by soaring medical costs and the increasingly stringent financial climate. Moreover, the claim that medical care, per se, has dramatically improved the overall health of the inhabitants of developed countries has increasingly been challenged. There is, in other words, a growing realisation that medical services may have had a relatively limited impact upon the major health problems of developed countries, whatever their impact may have been on individual patients. Instead, it is accepted that social and economic factors - often quite independent of medical care - have contributed significantly to changes in the overall pattern of disease.[5] Furthermore, since many of the diseases characteristic of modern societies, such as alcoholism, cancer, heart disease and accidents, have strong social determinants, it is at least probable that future improvements in health status will often result from changes that do not emanate from medical services.[6]

In this context, perhaps the most often cited critique of 'medicine as health' has come from Illich.[7] Not content to claim that the medical profession has become a major threat to health because of the ineffective, over-effective or harmful medicine practised, he has attacked also what he has termed the 'medicalisation of life'. Whether this challenge to the philosophical and clinical orientation of 'scientific medicine' will effect a change in provider behaviour is in some doubt, though commentators on the US scene suggest that a growing number of people are engaged in self-care practices, and that a number of practitioners (medical and other) are offering an increasingly wide range of therapies outside the mainstream of modern medical practice.[8]

This debate about the causal influences on health is well understood on a theoretical level by most health planners and policy-makers. However, the methods and means of putting it into practice are not. The Lalonde Report[9], while not necessarily leading or actively encouraging a revolution, none the less has served as a catalyst in focusing thinking upon health as a major public policy issue. In the terms of the Report, appropriate government action demands some prior analysis of the cause(s) of any given 'health' phenomenon, and a subsequent judgement on which key actors (individuals or corporate bodies) should be charged with, or approached to take, action. In essence, Lalonde argued that the 'health field' contained four elements - human biology, environment, life-style and health care - which, when taken together, provided a model for all relevant policy-making activities.

The significance of this work lay in its conclusion that greater attention had to be paid to the elements of human biology, environment and life-style, and rather less to health care, if real progress was to be made in reducing mortality and morbidity. It offered, in short, a tool to analyse health problems comprehensively, so that all aspects of health could be given due consideration, and all who contributed (the individual, government agencies, professional providers) could be made aware of their role and their degree of influence on health.

The concept of the 'health field' did, however, leave unconsidered the conditions to be satisfied before the different agencies would feel inclined to align their priorities and objectives to particular health issues. Giving priority to health objectives implies a failure to attain other, desired, objectives, and the risk of losing a degree of operating autonomy. In the circumstances, questions arise as to whether any one party can provide the solution to an agreed problem; whether

24

co-operation of several parties is required; and whether, in the absence of coercion, values and objectives can be shared between the parties, or incentives devised to stimulate the desired approach. In its defence, the health field concept does offer a means of defining the negotiating arena, identifying the potential parties to the negotiations, and establishing the limits to the contribution of medical care.

Three further obstacles in the way of fully embracing the concept of the health field can be identified. First, there are so many causal connections and organisational relationships to identify and order that the end result may present a picture too complex to be tackled. Second, the concept assumes that consumers will be prepared to accept the government's position that, for the community as a whole, a particular disease problem is not most effectively tackled by medical services, although such services may offer treatment beneficial to individual patients. Third, to approach health policy and planning in this way would require such a radical reorientation of outlook that most health service practitioners and governments would prefer to leave it as a Utopian ideal.[10] Thus, while the concept has considerable appeal at the level of intellectual conviction, these arguments suggest that the 'holistic' movement will forever stay out of the mainstream of policy.

It can none the less be argued that the one obvious and immediate outcome of the work of Illich, Lalonde and others is that they have prompted a more searching analysis of medicine: a recognition that the art and science of healing and caring do have dimensions that go beyond conventional medicine and that the promotion of health and prevention of ill health depend more on the nature of the environment and individuals' life-styles than hitherto has been acknowledged or appreciated. None the less, the organisation of health services is inextricably bound up with values and value judgements will continue to be made about what is health, and what health services should aim to provide. The difficulty of defining health and establishing the determinants of ill health means that there is agreement neither about the respective responsibilities of individuals and governments for health, nor about the means to be adopted by governments to tackle ill health, and this appears to be true in both developed and developing countries.

3 THE HEALTH SECTOR AND GOVERNMENT

The previous section implied that, given the variety of influences on health, the boundaries between the responsibilities for health and health services of the individual, the community, voluntary and governmental agencies will often be unclear. And yet it appears to be widely accepted that the development process needed to attain 'health for all' cannot be set up without widespread political commitment and action. Indeed, developed countries have experienced dramatic changes in the accepted scale and scope of government action in the health field. An initial concern with public protection measures, such as public health and environmental control, has expanded to acceptance of a wide range of collective social responsibilities.

In general, the acceptance by government of these responsibilities is said to arise from a belief that the efficient operation of private markets is unlikely in the health field.[11] Here, the argument is that a private market will not necessarily give correct signals of need to providers, and hence 'market failure' could occur, for the following reasons:

(1)   patients either do not recognise their symptoms or realise the consequences of not seeking treatment;

(2)   patients are generally unaware of the range and variety of health care alternatives available for treating a particular disease, and furthermore are not able to ascertain the benefits of treatment;

(3)   patients do not automatically or adequately consider their own state of health in terms of how they may enhance, or place at risk, the health and welfare of others; and

(4)   patients are deterred from seeking 'necessary' treatment by financial or other constraints.[12]

For these and doubtless other reasons, governments have found it necessary or appropriate to intervene in the health sector, believing it to be the case that private markets cannot be expected to allocate to health either the amount or the composition of resources that is best from a social perspective.

Government involvement in health matters, however, may take a variety of different forms: indeed, the range and permutation of possibilities are endless. A government may act as a regulator of independent health agencies; as a stimulator of research and pilot or demonstration projects; as a protector of deprived and disadvantaged groups; as a financier of health programmes and agencies; as a purchaser of health services and/or medical supplies; as a direct provider of services. These are all roles that have been adopted by governments, whether at a central or a local level, in different countries. At the very least, nations have established means to improve access to health services. In the United States, for example, despite the long-standing philosophy of market competition and pluralism, federal and state governments have provided subsidies to consumers and suppliers of health services and to those who train health care personnel and conduct research, and have directly provided services to particular population groups.

Increasing government involvement undoubtedly has contributed to the growth of health care expenditures, at a rate exceeding that of gross national product at least over recent decades, in all highly industrialised countries for which data are available. The typical pattern has been for an extra 1 per cent of national resources to be devoted to health care in the 1950s and a further 1.5 to 2 per cent in the 1960s.[13] In contrast, the 1970s and early 1980s are characterised by attempts to curb the rise in health care spending, whether or not such spending is publicly financed. To illustrate again from US experience, with total spending on medical care accounting by 1980 for approximately 9 per cent of GNP, there have been many calls for a reorganisation of the financing and organisation of medical and other health services. There are also calls for a continued growth of privately financed health maintenance organisations and pre-paid hospital and primary care services[14], as proven ways of providing a measure of cost containment. Many of the same concerns and arguments are exhibited in other countries.

What appears to be missing in these highly industrialised countries is any obvious correlation between the size of a country's health care expenditure and the state of its population's health. At an aggregate level, over the world as a whole, there is a clear negative correlation between infant mortality rates and both GNP per capita and health expenditure per capita.[15] If, however, only the richest countries are considered, such a correlation is not apparent. For instance, Sweden has the best (i.e. lowest) infant mortality rate and the longest expectation of life, but the United States, with somewhat higher per capita expenditure than Sweden, holds a much lower position than the UK in the international mortality league table. As noted already, health is a product of so many factors, of which the availability and consumption of health services is only one part, that it is difficult to prove any causal connection between levels of expenditure and states of health.[16]

What is, none the less, clear is that the long-term growth of health expenditure - not only absolutely but also relative to gross domestic product - has been a feature common to most industrialised countries. In developing countries, fragmentary evidence suggests that as much as 6 to 10 per cent of the GDP is spent by governments and households on health care.[17] Moreover, consumer demand for improved health services is more or less universally expressed. Yet, how much of any country's resources are devoted to publicly financed health services is a matter for political decision, constrained by the availability of government revenues. It must be expected, therefore, that public expectations and limits to the government purse will have to be accommodated, and health policies devised accordingly.

4 POLICY ANALYSIS AND HEALTH POLICY-MAKING

While the meaning of the term 'health' has been considered already, the term 'policy' remains to be investigated. Two sharply differing interpretations can be identified. The first and more common usage defines health policies as authoritative statements of intent, probably adopted by governments on behalf of the public, with the aim of altering for the better the health and welfare of the population. Health policy, in this sense, implies a 'centrally' determined basis for action, designed to alter some situation, system, practice or behaviour towards given ends.

In contrast, a quite different approach to the conceptualisation of health policy stems from recognition of the existence of multiple decision-makers, including those at the 'periphery', and of conflicting interests. From this point of view, health policy is defined as what health agencies actually do, rather than what governments would like them to do. If so, health policy can be determined only by examining the outcomes of decision-making, and hence the accommodations and patterns of dominance prevailing both within and between organisations.[18]

In either interpretation, it is clear that the content of health policy will always be value-laden, as in the two following examples. In the first place, budgetary restraints and cut-backs in health services expenditure in both North America and Western Europe have created opposition amongst the medical profession and other health care workers, who are unlikely to remain neutral about their right to work and to influence the allocation of resources. Second, in many developing countries, national health policy statements have shifted perceptibly towards primary health care and away from hospital-based services, towards the rural and urban poor and by implication away from urban elites. In both of these examples, new government objectives have been reflected in policy documents and health plans, but in many instances their values have not been shared by agencies or actors within the health system, and thus significant changes in the actual delivery of services and in provider behaviour have been slow to appear.

In continuing the discussion of the formulation of policies and plans and their subsequent degree of implementation, it is helpful to distinguish between analysis of policy and analysis for policy. This distinction can be made clear in terms of a continuum or range of activities, all of which can be said to fall under the rubric of 'policy analysis' (see Figure 1).[19]

Figure 1: Policy Analysis, by Type of Activity

Analysis for policy			Analysis of policy	
Policy Advocacy	Information for Policy	Policy Monitoring and Evaluation	Analysis of Policy Determination	Analysis of Policy Content

The five types which can be identified in the policy analysis literature are:

(1)   literature in the normative tradition which directly advocates a particular policy direction;

(2)   literature in the analytical and theoretical traditions which provides policy-makers with information, and perhaps advice, to assist the formulation of appropriate policies;

(3)   literature that monitors and evaluates policy, as a post hoc analysis of policies and programmes;

(4)   literature that provides an analysis of policy determination in terms of how health policies are formulated and constructed; and, finally,

(5)   literature that takes as its primary concern the analysis of policy content, that is the study of the intentions and operation of specific policies.

The role of these various types of policy analysis in decision-making depends upon the structure of decision-making and the incentives which guide each of the decision-makers.[20] Necessarily, policy-making is concerned both with what is politically feasible and what is technically desirable. Does this imply that policies are informed by the careful examination of problems and a full review of possible solutions? Or do they emerge from a confused battleground of ideas, values, individual preferences and expediency?[21]

These questions suggest that it is possible to trace at least two ways in which the analysis of problems may be related to the taking of decisions. First, there is what may be termed the 'ideal' or apparently 'technical' process, whereby policy choices are enlightened by an 'impartial' analysis of the value of policies and their costs, as well as of the distribution of these effects among various subgroups in the population. 'Information for policy' and 'policy monitoring and evaluation' would form an integral part of such a policy analysis, and participants in that process would require and rely upon such analysis to guide their decisions. While such an ideal is

29

self-evidently a counsel of perfection, it can provide a benchmark for evaluating the policy process.

The second approach, by contrast, suggests that policy-making is better served if goals are left implicit or vague, and if policy action is seen not as the outcome of explicit choice but rather as the result of bargaining between individuals and groups. Policy-makers operating according to this model are likely to be unwilling to specify clear objectives, partly because of their own doubts about the ends of health policy, but also because they profit from retaining a degree of ambiguity and hence freedom of manoeuvre.[22]

In summary, it is clear that the policy process is complex and thus open to a number of different interpretations.[23] There is unlikely to be one single explanation of the determination or execution of any particular health policy. However, whether the political and the more analytical phases of policy-making can be viewed as distinct stages must be seriously in doubt.

5 THE RATIONALE FOR HEALTH PLANNING

Planning systems can be considered to provide a means whereby policies will be translated into action. The planning process, therefore, can be defined to include policy analysis and, indeed, many of the ideas considered above are as applicable to planning as they are to policy analysis, and the two fields have some literature in common. The standard definition of planning is usually phrased in such terms as: 'the process of deciding how the future should be different from the present, what changes are necessary, and how these changes should be brought about'. Planning, as understood in this context, is likely to be concerned with complex situations, and with a time horizon some years into the future: the organisation of simple, immediate events does not demand an elaborate planning process.

Planning also embraces the basic assumptions that a calculated intervention will improve the future, and that future events can in some fashion be predicted. Hence, key concepts in planning are likely to be those of 'complexity', 'objectives' and 'time horizon'. Calculated interventions involve forecasting, the exercise of judgement and decision-making. Whatever analytical techniques are used, planning is ultimately concerned with making decisions about what must be done in order to make a desired future possible.

But why does a belief in the desirability of conscious intervention to mould the future exist? A number of reasons for planning have been suggested, though the introduction of a new or improved planning system at one point in time will be due to a variety of reasons[24], which will differ from country to country. The possible reasons for adopting a formal planning system can be generalised in the following way:

(1) Resource considerations - planning is often seen as a means of making full use of scarce resources. In developing countries, finance and skilled manpower are usually extremely scarce, and the tax base of the economy is likely to be very limited. In developed countries, concern about the scarcity of resources stems from the continual growth of high-cost, capital-intensive and hospital-based medical care.

(2) Territorial considerations - in many countries, both in the developed and in the Third World, planning is seen to offer a way of counteracting perceived geographical inequities in access to, and supply of, medical care, especially for rural populations and the urban poor.

(3) Priority considerations - planning is seen as a means of redirecting priorities away from high-technology medical care and towards neglected areas such as primary care, preventive medicine, mental health and diseases associated with ageing.

(4) Arbitrating considerations - the planning process is seen as a means of mediating between competing claims for resources, and also of constraining the behaviour of certain providers who might otherwise dominate.[25]

In these terms, planning is evidently about choice: choice of desirable objectives, choice of one future rather than another, and choice between various ways of achieving that future. It is clear, therefore, that planning is both a political and social process for identifying and reconciling the values of interested parties in order to establish goals and objectives, and also a technical process of forecasting and evaluating options in the light of agreed values and expected constraints.

But is this too comfortable a summary? Can values be so readily agreed and can the constraints be overcome? Preoccupation with the formal elements of a planning system can obscure the process by which such planning actually takes place, and the differing interpretations given to planning. Some may see planning as a worthwhile attempt to mould and control the future, others may see it as a means of coping with conflicts, yet others may consider it undesirable, irrelevant or impossible. What then are the likely constraints any planning system will face?

6 BASIC ASSUMPTIONS IN HEALTH PLANNING

Health planning is based on certain underlying assumptions, whose strength, or otherwise, will influence greatly the success of planning within any country's health sector.[26]

Political Stability

In the broad sense planning is political, for it is concerned with the creation and implementation of health policies. It is therefore vulnerable to changes in political direction as may occur, for instance, when governments change. This problem may not arise when there is a continuing political consensus over health and social welfare goals. However, in some countries, a change of government may herald so drastic a change in policies that plans will have to be rewritten. Frequent government changes or a high degree of political instability may make a nonsense of any attempt to undertake long-term planning.

Economic Stability

The orientation of planning towards the future makes it dependent not only on some degree of political stability but also, and in some respects perhaps more crucially, on economic stability. Planners in the public sector need to feel some assurance that public expenditure projections in general, and projections for the health budget in particular, are reliable. Moreover, planning has to be sufficiently robust, for instance by using a range of resource assumptions to formulate alternative scenarios, to withstand high levels of inflation, sudden escalations in capital or drug costs, or changes in resource availability. Failure to do so may threaten the credibility of planning, for instance when unexpected additional resources are spent in ways incompatible with existing plans.

Will and Compliance

Reference has been made already to the demands that planning makes on actors and agencies to incorporate long-term thinking into their day-to-day behaviour. This will not come easily to everyone, especially when advantage is gained by retaining freedom of action. Thus the provision of a legislative basis for health planning agencies, or the official introduction of a planning system, will not by themselves ensure the willingness of all participants to work through a planning system. Moreover, as stressed already, for planning decisions to be translated into action, it is necessary for decision-makers to satisfy themselves on the compliance of those who are affected by their decisions. Planning, in consequence, depends on formulating viable courses of action which attract both the will and the compliance of all interested parties.[27]

Technical Infrastructure

Hence, it would appear that the technical input to planning is likely to be ineffective if divorced from pragmatic considerations of political interest and political demands for information and analysis.[28] None the less, planning will have little chance of success unless appropriate methodologies and techniques are available to produce relevant and accurate information for politicians and interest groups, and to formulate and evaluate plans; and unless competent personnel in the relevant disciplines are employed in adequate numbers. Likewise, it will be necessary for there to be a well developed organisational structure to sustain the planning activity.

7 ORIGINS AND DEVELOPMENT OF HEALTH PLANNING

The aim of this section is to identify, albeit in skeleton form, the thinking behind the movement towards formal health planning systems in the USA and UK. The corporate planning movement is usually considered to have started in a number of large private organisations[29] faced with the problems of organisational size and complexity, high capital intensity and sensitivity (if not vulnerability) to technological change. Such characteristics led these organisations to look for improved co-ordination between divisions; an efficient management of growth; a sound investment policy; and a secure mechanism for anticipating technological change. Corporate planning was developed as a means of directly addressing these issues, and was considered to bring the following benefits:

(1)   it forced management to think systematically about the future;
(2)   it created a sense of direction;
(3)   it provided criteria for assessing proposals for expansion and contraction; and
(4)   it provided a basis for resource planning (especially finance and manpower).

By the mid-1960s, WHO began to show interest in transferring corporate planning ideas to the health sector, and interest in health planning was developing also in the UK and US. Indeed, these two countries provide useful illustrations of how health planning has been introduced into very different health care systems.

United Kingdom

In the UK, few attempts were made at any long-term planning of health and welfare services before the 1970s. What planning there was in the 1950s and 1960s arose from the concern of central government to promote or guide capital building programmes for such sectors as hospitals, schools, universities and housing. There were in addition some initial attempts, largely abortive, to plan the supply of teachers and doctors. From the mid-1960s, however, policy analysis and planning, albeit of a rather rudimentary sort, began to be introduced as the general policy-making environment changed.[30] First, the introduction and gradual extension of the system of public expenditure and control (PESC) after 1961, and especially after 1968, obliged spending departments of central government to justify their bids for Treasury finance with medium-term forecasts of costs and demands. Second, the Treasury had itself set up a five-year rolling projection of government spending plans, against which departmental claims for extra resources were vetted. Third, from the early 1970s these central departments began to extend their planning and policy processes to local government and local health authorities.

As a result, the 1970s saw a peak in British planning activity in the social welfare field, with a complex range of formal planning procedures developed by central and local government and by public bodies. Indeed, it has been estimated that by the end of that decade there were well over twenty 'public policy systems' in operation, each with its own timetable, procedures and information requirements.[31]

The particular arguments put forward for the NHS Planning System[32], introduced formally in 1976 and in existence since that time, included:

(1) the need to counteract previously identified short-comings, such as the inadequate consideration of the resource implications of decisions; the bias towards capital developments; the piecemeal approach to priorities; and the lack of attention to 'total patient care';

(2) the belief that planning would be the best means of co-ordinating and integrating health services;

(3) the need for a means by which central control could be exercised over the NHS as required by statute;

(4) the need for a mechanism to consult interested parties on key issues;

(5) the view that the planning system would lead to better informed and more considered decisions, and contribute to the removal of inequalities and inequities in the provision of health services and in health itself.

These various arguments can be sorted into two rather different views about the rationale for a health services planning system in the UK. One view would see a more formal planning approach as a response to the scale and complexity of issues in the health sector. Certainly, it is this perspective that was emphasised in the official accounts. Planning was seen as the means by which health authorities could learn about the needs of the population to be served, and create strategies whereby priorities could be balanced and put into effect within available resources.

The alternative view would be that, whatever the ideals of health planning, the planning procedures within the UK (as some official documents imply) have more to do with developing a system of management and financial control than with identifying health care needs. Certainly, it is possible to see health planning in the UK from the late 1970s as strongly influenced by the government's attempt to come to terms with the rationing dilemma posed by the mismatch between health care needs and resource availability. Hence, planning was also seen as an explicit and centralised rationing and control procedure.

In terms of the economic aspects of health planning, two particular factors assume considerable importance: the containment of overall costs and obtaining better value from a given health care expenditure. Which of these two factors assumes prominence within a country at any point in time will depend crucially upon political concerns and economic considerations. In the UK in the early 1980s, it is the list of services to be provided and funded by the public sector that is being held up to the closest scrutiny. Rationing and cost control appear therefore for the moment to be seen, by central decision-makers, as the most important tasks of health planning.

United States

Some critics of the American medical care system would argue, even today, that it is in reality a non-system. However, some historical parallels with the UK do exist[33], and can be drawn out most clearly by documenting the important stages by which the US has moved away from notions of voluntary planning towards a regulatory form of government involvement in health care. Since the beginning of the federal government's involvement in the 1940s, the objectives, scope and organisation of planning have been determined by government policy largely through a series of programmes:

> The provisions of the programs and the experiences of the processes they established are milestones in the transformation of health planning from its origins in elite-dominated, categorised planning to the present participatory, comprehensive planning, and from planning in the absence of regulation to the partial joining of these functions.[34]

Prior to the 1940s, health planning was limited to localised efforts aimed primarily at co-ordinating public health and hospital activities. However, in the 1940s the poor condition of many hospitals prompted the federal government to establish the nation's first major health services planning and construction subsidy programme, the Hill-Burton Program (1946). Over the next twenty years, this programme was considered to be more successful in distributing construction funds to hospitals than in planning co-operation between hospitals. Partly as a remedy for this deficiency, the Regional Medical Programs Act was passed in 1965 and Regional Advisory Groups (RAGs) were set up in 56 regions throughout the United States to devise plans. However, provider interests were heavily represented on the groups, state governments were given no role in the programme's implementation or funding, and RAGs concentrated at least initially on a few disease categories.

No agency had responsibility for comprehensive health planning until legislation was passed in 1966 for a network of voluntary comprehensive health planning agencies with tasks of developing long-range, state-wide and local plans for environmental as well as personal health services. However, the Act specified that planning was to be accomplished without any corresponding regulatory authority: in effect, CHP agencies were to be set up and given the mandate to develop plans, but not the means to implement them. At best they could practise only 'consensus' planning.

By the early 1970s, concern about the over-supply of hospital beds had removed the raison d'être for Hill-Burton, and the Regional Medical Programs and the Comprehensive Health Planning Program were widely considered to be of limited success. In consequence, the National Health Planning and Resources Development Act, currently the nation's principal health planning legislation, was passed in 1974.

This Act made an explicit statement about many of the underlying problems in the health care system: inequality of access to health services; maldistribution of resources; over-emphasis on hospitalisation; consumer ignorance; and the need for regionalisation of health services, alternative methods of health care delivery, and more emphasis upon prevention. To deal with these issues, the basic element was to be a nation-wide system of Health Systems Agencies (HSAs), non-profit corporations made up of representatives of the public, providers, payers and politicians, though the majority were to be consumer representatives. Most important, perhaps, was the re- quirement that each agency generate both long-range comprehensive plans and shorter-range plans for implementing the long-term strategies. Finally, the programme gave regulatory functions to HSAs through the use of 'certificate of need' legislation. These certificates, dating from earlier legislation in 1972, represented a major shift in emphasis for health planning in the United States. For the first time, health planning had a weapon in the form of financial restriction, or denial, that could be invoked if changes in capital developments, or changes in services, did not conform with the needs as documented in each state's health plans.

As might have been expected, these developments did not meet with universal acclaim, or success. One view is that planning and regulation have been largely ineffective because the strategy was pursued only half-heartedly; another that planning and regulation are inherently clumsy. Certainly the legislation has exacerbated the conflict in American society between devotion to the virtues of the 'market' as the bedrock of the economy and widespread reliance upon increasingly stringent regulatory controls. Over the decade of the 1970s it appeared that planning was more an attempt at cost containment (i.e. rationing and control) than a positive force for innovation in health care delivery and health promotion. In the early 1980s, even that more limited public role is to be reviewed by the federal government. Whether health planning will be given both the national commitment and the federal financial support to give it time to 'grow, adjust and mature' is very unclear.[35]

The above brief accounts of planning in the USA and UK suggest that the planning styles in the two countries are coming closer together than might be expected from the history of their respective health systems: in particular, from the more atomistic image held of society in the United States, as against a more holistic and public approach in Britain. Both countries have paid homage to the virtues of comprehensive planning, and there may be grounds for believing that differences in their health systems may further be minimised by the end of the 1980s, if the concern of their respective governments continues to focus on regulatory and financial control mechanisms.

8 SUMMARY AND CONCLUSION

The features of health planning and policy-making, as identified in this chapter, can be summarised as follows. Planning is future-oriented, in contrast to the day-to-day management process; it is a political and social process as well as a technical process; it incorporates the evaluation of options against agreed values and expected constraints; and, finally, it is a continuing process whereby an evaluation of the implementation of health policies becomes a prerequisite to future planning activity.

The conventional conclusion from such a summary is that planning, while necessarily fallible - given an unknowable future - is still the best means of coping with uncertainty. But is it? There are likely to be limits to governments' and individuals' tolerance of planning as a worthwhile activity, bearing in mind that natural instincts and inclinations focus attention on the immediate and the imminent rather than the more distant; and that rewards and remuneration are normally similarly linked. Yet arguments advanced for planning in many different settings all reflect a desire for an orderly and systematic approach to health sector development. However, for many developed countries a previously optimistic scenario has changed with a shift in the economic climate. The conventional wisdom is now to demonstrate, as has been argued for some time in developing countries, that health planning is even more important in circumstances of tight financial constraints. Some commentators have concluded that economic restraint will encourage greater 'rationality'; others are less sanguine. Later chapters in this book will attempt to test the claims made for planning against health planning in practice.

NOTES

1. WHO, 'Formulating Strategies for Health for All by the Year 2000' (WHO, Geneva, 1979).
2. World Bank, 'Health: Sector Policy Paper', 2nd edn (World Bank, Washington, DC, February 1980).
3. H. Mahler, Health for All by the Year 2000, 'World Health' (February/March 1981).
4. B. Abel-Smith and A. Leiserson, Poverty, Development, and Health Policy, 'Public Health Paper 69' (WHO, Geneva, 1978).
5. T. McKeown, 'The Role of Medicine: Dream, Mirage, or Nemesis?' (The Nuffield Provincial Hospitals Trust, London, 1976).
6. J. B. McKinlay, Epidemiological and Political Determinants of Social Policies Regarding the Public Health, 'Social Science and Medicine', vol. 13A (1979), pp. 541-58.
7. I. Illich, 'Medical Nemesis: the Expropriation of Health' (Calder and Boyars, London, 1975).
8. J. W. Salmon and H. S. Berliner, Health Policy Implications of the Holistic Health Movement, 'Journal of Health Politics, Policy and Law', vol. 5, no. 3 (Fall 1980), pp. 535-53.
9. M. Lalonde, 'A New Perspective on the Health of Canadians' (Government of Canada, Ottawa, 1974).
10. K. Barnard, Comprehensive Health Planning - the State of the Art, 'Community Medicine', vol. 129, no. 19 (23 February 1973), pp. 375-8.
11. T. Bice, Health Services Planning and Regulation in S. J. Williams and P. R. Torrens (eds.), 'Introduction to Health Services' (Wiley, New York, 1980).
12. K. Lee, Need Versus Demand: the Planner's Dilemma in K. Lee (ed.), 'Economics and Health Planning' (Croom Helm,

London, 1979), pp. 45-69.

13. B. Abel-Smith, Health Care in a Cold Economic Climate, 'The Lancet', 14 February 1981, pp. 373-6.

14. G. Parston, 'Planners, Politics and Health Services' (Croom Helm, London, 1980).

15. G. Cumper, 'Primary Health Care and the Availability of Resources for Health Development', reference paper for WHO/UNICEF Interregional Workshop on Cost and Financing Patterns of Primary Health Care, Geneva, 1-5 December 1980.

16. K. Lee, Public Expenditure, Health Services, and Health in A. Walker (ed.), 'Public Expenditure and Social Priorities' (Heinemann, London, 1981).

17. World Bank, 'Health', p. 19.

18. T. A. Booth (ed.), 'Planning for Welfare: Social Policy and the Expenditure Process' (Basil Blackwell and Martin Robertson, Oxford, 1979).

19. I. Gordon, J. Lewis and K. Young, Perspectives on Policy Analysis, 'Public Administration Bulletin', no. 25 (1977), pp. 26-35.

20. R. H. Haveman, Policy Analysis and the Congress: an Economist's View in R. H. Haveman and J. Margolis (eds.), 'Public Expenditure and Policy Analysis', 2nd edn (Rand McNally College Publishing Company, Chicago, 1977); reprinted from 'Policy Analysis', vol. 2, no. 2 (Spring 1976), pp. 235-50.

21. P. Hall, H. Land, R. Parker and A. Webb, 'Change, Choice and Conflict in Social Policy' (Heinemann, London, 1975).

22. J. Higgins, The Unfulfilled Promise of Policy Research, 'Social Policy and Administration', vol. 14, no. 3 (Autumn 1980), pp. 195-208.

23. C. Ham, Approaches to the Study of Social Policy Making, 'Policy and Politics', vol. 8, no. 1 (1980), pp. 55-71.

24. E. J. Razzell, Planning in Whitehall - Is it Possible? - Will it Survive?, 'Long Range Planning', vol. 13 (February 1980), pp. 34-41.

25. T. R. Marmor and A. Bridges, American Health Planning and the Lessons of Comparative Policy Analysis, 'Journal of Health Politics, Policy and Law', vol. 5, no. 3 (Fall 1980), pp. 419-30.

26. A. Waterston, An Operational Approach to Development Planning, 'International Journal of Health Services', vol. 1, no. 3 (1971), pp. 233-52.

27. K. Barnard, Health Planning: the Last of the Panaceas, in K. Barnard and K. Lee (eds.), 'NHS Reorganisation: Issues and Prospects' (University of Leeds, Leeds, 1974).

28. J. Forester, Critical Theory and Planning Practice, 'American Planning Association Journal' (July 1980), pp. 275-86.

29. J. Thackray, Planning's Future Shock, 'Management Today'

(September 1973).

30. R. Klein, The Rise and Decline of Policy Analysis: the Strange Case of Health Policymaking in Britain, 'Policy Analysis', vol. 2, no. 3 (Summer 1976), pp. 459-75.
31. H. Glennerster, From Containment to Conflict? - Social Planning in the Seventies, 'Journal of Social Policy', vol. 10, no. 1 (1981), pp. 31-51.
32. DHSS, 'The NHS Planning System' (HMSO, London, 1976).
33. K. Lee, Political Economy of Health Care in England in G. I. Misek (ed.), 'Socioeconomic Issues of Health 1979' (American Medical Association, Chicago, Illinois, 1979).
34. Bice, Health Services Planning and Regulation, p. 329.
35. H. P. Cain, Health Planning in the United States: the 1980s - a Protagonist's View, 'Journal of Health Politics, Policy and Law', vol. 6, no. 1 (1981), pp. 159-71.

3 THEORIES OF HEALTH PLANNING

1 INTRODUCTION

World-wide interest in developing planning systems for the health sector has been stimulated by an increasing awareness that many of the major health care issues remain unresolved. These include: growing concerns about the magnitude of future demands upon health services; the increased financial stringency which has exacerbated the problems of meeting all health needs; and the growing doubts on the efficiency and effectiveness of many current forms of health care delivery. The result has been an increasing popularity for health planning as an apparently useful tool for improving health services and, presumably therefore, health. This popularity has been accompanied by high expectations that it is indeed possible to develop strategies for attacking health and welfare issues.

Although few people would deny the usefulness of planning, controversies do exist over what form planning should take - its range, scope and likely effectiveness. This chapter, therefore, examines the possible reasons why formalising the planning process has appeared desirable to many in the health sector, explores how that formalisation might be conceived, and offers some observations on the necessary and sufficient conditions for the success of formalisation.

At the outset, it can be acknowledged that not only is there no universally agreed classification of planning theories, but general agreement on what 'planning' means is reached only at the highest level of generalisation. When planning is described as 'deciding how the future should be different from the present, what changes are necessary, and how these changes should be brought about', few eyebrows are raised. If, however, attempts are made to determine who decides, and the means or strategies by which such changes should take place, attitudes to planning fall into a number of distinct schools, each reflecting a particular philosophy and definition of planning.

Theoretical models often view health planning as a detailed and rational corporate attempt to handle broad societal issues. But, in recent years, there has been increasing criticism of this dominant planning theory - the rational planning model - though it is still widely taught to potential planners, and frequently adopted as a desirable model by governments and

41

international agencies. In practice, critics note, health planning tends to be incremental, and takes the form of an institutionalised bargaining system which neglects the larger issues in favour of marginal adjustments. The strength of this view lies in its recognition that plans are necessarily the outcome of the behaviour and decision-making processes of governments and health agencies, groups and individuals.

Whether and how planning models can fit into an essentially political decision-making process is, therefore, of critical importance. Certainly, the political tools of decision-making - bargaining, advocacy, negotiation and compromise - are important means by which plans are likely both to be developed and implemented. From that perspective, it is argued in this chapter that mixed scanning, the detailed examination of selected, feasible proposals, might combine the best features of theory and practice. It is also argued that successful implementation hinges upon the identification of powerful interest groups (such as politicians, doctors and managers), of their motives and likely behaviour, and upon the existence and use of incentives to guide their activities.

Before any assessment can be made of the likely success or failure of national, regional or local approaches to health planning, it is appropriate first to review the various planning models that exist, set out their main features, and look for pointers to the likely opportunities or difficulties that might be encountered in putting them into practice. That, in short, is the purpose of this chapter.

2   FUTURES STUDIES VERSUS PLANNING

Prior to considering the various planning models, it is worth noting that there is some confusion in the literature between 'planning' and 'futures studies' which is of more than semantic importance. What underlies the study of the future is the view that not only is it possible to explore and assess the future, but that it is vital to do this in order to alert management and government to the possibilities and probabilities that the future holds. The broadest objection to any attempt to study the future is that it is impossible; but this line of reasoning, while not without some foundation, does not rule out the development of a range of alternative futures which can help set the limits for debate about health services and health.[1]

The most general approach to the study of the future is known as social forecasting or futures studies. It is claimed that the two features that distinguish futures studies from planning are the time horizon and the base-line for analysis. First, although both are concerned with the future, futures studies necessarily take a longer time horizon. Second, planning is based on the present, and often the past, and looks forward; futures studies, in contrast, attempt to take the future as the base-line and look backward to the present.[2]

Planning, in this definition, therefore, tries to set out what will be, given certain historically based assumptions; while futures is about alternatives - what possible futures might exist, and how likely they are to materialise. The significance of this distinction is as follows. Futures studies can be regarded as providing a context for decision-making, to illuminate and provide background for policy-makers; they do not of themselves represent decisions. In contrast, planning is a particular kind of decision-making, in that the planning process requires that a decision be made by managers on whether to accept, reject, amend or ignore the plans formulated.

3 A PLANNING CONTINUUM

Over the last twenty years or so, a considerable number of planning theories have been advanced [3] and, although there is seemingly a good deal of agreement among theorists about how planning and policy-making have been undertaken in practice, there is less consensus about how these activities should be conducted. The three main approaches to planning that have emerged, and which can be related to the health sector, are usually referred to as 'Rational', 'Incremental' and 'Mixed Scanning' theories.[4]

These theories tend to categorise policy-making along a continuum, the extremities of which are marked by notions of 'incrementalism' and 'rationalism'.

'Rationalism'   'Mixed Scanning'   'Incrementalism'

Necessarily, the degree of 'rationality' or otherwise is likely to vary from instance to instance, such that in practice there will be a number of intermediate staging posts or modes of planning.

The 'rational' approach demands that the decision-maker identifies the goals or objectives that should govern the choice of solution to the problem, and undertakes a comprehensive review of all possible alternatives and their merits and de-merits. On this basis, a solution is chosen as a master plan for maximising the objectives consciously selected. 'Incrementalist' approaches of planning, by contrast, emphasise the traditional bureaucratic methods of marginal, disjointed decisions, or 'muddling through' as it has been termed. These approaches conclude that only those policies which differ incrementally from existing ones will be, and perhaps should be, considered. Policies are seen to be the outcome of mutual adjustment among the interests involved in the decision-making process. Concerns that 'rationalism' is a distant ideal and that 'incrementalism' as a deliberate strategy is limited have led to the formulation of a third approach, of 'mixed scanning', in which a broad scan of the sector is undertaken first, in order to identify which decisions might continue to be taken on an 'incremental' basis and which require a more 'rational' approach.[5]

In dealing with this continuum, the important consideration is to determine whether, under a particular set of circumstances, planning practice will move towards rationalism, and whether, under a different set of circumstances, planning will become the outcome of bargaining. In other words, when does incrementalism stop being incremental? Where are the dividing lines between incrementalism, mixed scanning and rationality?[6]

4 RATIONALISM

Much of the literature on planning commences with the 'rational' model, in the belief either that organisations do exhibit behaviour that can be termed 'rational', or that the model does at the very least provide a reference point from which to start. A 'rational' decision can be described as one made in the following manner:

(1) the decision-maker lists all the opportunities for action open to him;

(2) he identifies all the consequences which would follow from the adoption of each of the possible actions; and

(3) he selects that course of action that maximises output for a given input, or minimises input for a given output.

Expressed in the purest terms, rational decision-making can be described as a process of logic; there is a known objective that the decision-maker wishes to achieve, the decision-maker has to choose between several known alternative ways of achieving this objective, the consequences of each alternative are also known, and the decision-maker, given this information, can choose the alternative which is best for him.[7] More practically, a rational decision is one in which alternatives and consequences are considered as fully as the decision-maker, given the time and other resources available to him, can afford to consider them.

But what is 'rationality'? It is important to distinguish between the different dimensions of rationality, for rationality is not a concept characterised by a single value. A particular decision might have been politically rational, in the sense that any other action would have created unacceptably large political costs. It may also have been administratively rational in the sense of keeping a service running rather than changing it, thereby minimising disruption in a complex system. But could it be called rational in any other sense?[8] The general models of rationality usually assume that the decision-maker is the judge of rationality. Yet his basic difficulties and room for manoeuvre derive from value conflicts between interested parties, from the frequently confused interaction between values and facts in policy issues, and from the great uncertainty about outcomes.

A further issue concerns how widely the net of health planning should be cast. Some proponents of health planning see it as a means of rationalising the provision of medical care, and as a way of redistributing resources more appropriately to given ends. As Chapter 2 has shown, others look more widely, seeking to determine the relationship between what is primarily a medical care system and a wide range of other services, such as personal social services, education, environmental control and housing, relevant to the health and well-being of the community. Proponents of this wider approach would claim that, since health services cannot be considered in isolation from the rest of our social fabric and institutions, attempts to plan and develop health services in vacuo will be unlikely to improve the health of the population. Should the planners of health services therefore take due note of these 'external' factors and public and private agencies? If so, how?

Certainly, rational planning models in the public sector have come to be identified with comprehensive and corporate attempts to handle broad social problems. Indeed, the world-wide movement towards the establishment of formal health planning systems may be viewed as a recognition both of the deficiencies of previous uncoordinated health care practices and of the merits of more 'rational' approaches to health service planning and policy-making.

In the USA the rational planning model provided the basis for much of the health planning legislation that emerged from the health programmes of the 1960s. Comprehensive Health Planning, Regional Medical Programs and Experimental Health Service Delivery Systems were all based on the premiss that needs could be assessed and public resources allocated rationally. For CHP, the objective was allocation by larger planning areas, for RMP it was rational allocation of hospital resources, for EHSDS the goal was the rational integration of public and private resources.[9]

Somewhat late in the history of the English NHS it became increasingly recognised that, given the enormity of the task of health care provision and the magnitude of the resources involved, it would seem imprudent, at the least, to leave major issues entirely to chance or to the uncoordinated actions of numerous bodies. Accordingly, a corporate planning system was developed and introduced into the NHS in 1976, and covered both the Department of Health and Social Security (DHSS) and Health Authorities. Prior to 1976 health planning, in terms of corporate and comprehensive approaches to decision-making, had been more a matter of discussion than practice.[10] In the future, it was expected that rational policy-making would emerge, resulting in the setting of explicit policy objectives, linked to specific financial targets, and the monitoring of progress towards their achievement.

Experimentation with rational policy-making in health care has not been confined to North America and the UK. According to a recent WHO publication[11], most countries already have some form of 'managerial process for national health development' which, despite wide variations in detail, have certain components in common. These components are illustrated in Figure 2, and are:

(1)   The formulation of national health policies – comprising goals, priorities and main directions for reaching priority goals – that are suitable to the social needs and economic conditions of the country and form part of national social and economic development policies.

(2)   Broad programming – the translation of these policies, through various stages of planning, into strategies to achieve clearly stated objectives and, wherever possible, specific targets.

(3)   Programme budgeting – the preferential allocation of health resources for the implementation of these strategies.

(4)   The master plan of action resulting from broad programming and programme budgeting that indicates the strategies to be followed, and the main lines of action to be taken in the health and other sectors to implement these strategies.

(5)   Detailed programming – the conversion of strategies and plans of action into detailed programmes that specify objectives, targets, technology, manpower, infrastructure, financial resources and time required to implement programmes.

(6)   Implementation – the translation of detailed programmes into action so that they become operational as integral parts of the health system; the day-to-day management of programmes and the services and institutions for delivering them; and the continuing follow-up of activities to ensure that they are proceeding as planned and are on schedule.

(7)   Evaluation of developmental health strategies and operational programmes, in order progressively to improve their effectiveness and impact and increase their efficiency.

(8)   Reprogramming, as necessary, with a view to

improving the master plan of action or some of its components, or preparing new ones as required, as a part of a continuous managerial process.

(9)   The provision of relevant and sensitive information to support all these components.

These steps provide a good example of the now familiar and well established model of the rational planning process, and are presented by WHO in a neat, systematic way.

Figure 2: Managerial Process for National Health Development

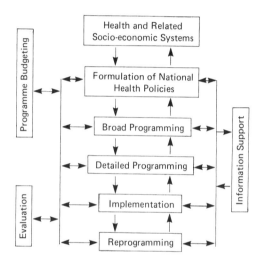

Source: WHO, 'Guiding Principles for the Managerial Process for National Health Development' (WHO, Geneva, September 1980).

The rational planning model is thus both officially advocated and widely adopted. Yet it has been widely criticised, both as a description of decision-making and as a prescription of how decisions should be reached. Critics challenge the assumptions of the rational model that governments and organisations can state their goals in precise and realistic terms; that they know the full range of alternatives available to them and their respective costs and benefits; and that they are able freely to choose the optimal or best solution. Rather, observers incline to the view that in practice there is very little planning, and even less rationality.[12]

Among the compelling arguments against the likely existence of planning and rationality in any government or organisation is that, theoretically, the rationalist strategy demands full knowledge of the consequences of all alternative courses of action, full knowledge of all cause and effect relationships and complete agreement on the goals to be pursued. The real world, of course, defies any attempts to reduce it to such simple dimensions. To that extent, the model is an unworkable concept if taken literally; and, if so taken, the results will be no more than elegant blueprints that gather dust but no commitment from interested parties.

Hence, critics challenge the classic rational model on the grounds that it overestimates the decision-maker's intellectual capacities and the quality and quantity of available data. In addition, it can be argued that, rather than being confronted with a limited range of alternatives and a stable set of values, decision-makers face an open set of variables. Values are fluid and are affected by, as well as effect, the decisions made. Necessarily, there will be 'political' problems in the harmonisation of values between the interested or affected parties, especially in the health sector where governments often need to seek a compromise among essentially incompatible interests.

The very nature of rational health planning is, in short, its biggest difficulty. If decision-makers are expected to take account of everything in sight they will, by trying to look at everything, see nothing in particular. Information about consequences is, at best, partial. Decision-makers have neither the resources, the time nor the incentive to collect the information required for 'rational' choice. It is all too easy to see that in the face of the demands of the rational model, decision-makers will be motivated to simplify, to look for more feasible approaches to planning and decision-making.

5 INCREMENTALISM

If the 'rational' model of planning does not conform to reality, or even form the basis of an ideal type of planning, what can be offered in its place? A less demanding model of decision-making outlined by Lindblom - the so-called 'strategy of disjointed incrementalism' - is a potential candidate, inasmuch as it is designed to overcome the weaknesses of a 'synoptic' approach.[13]

The theory starts from the premiss that rational decision-making is not possible. Governments and organisations are unable to classify values or objectives and identify and evaluate all alternative ways of realising them. The argument is, therefore, that attempts at comprehensive problem-solving in complex organisations are irrational in that they assume capacities of analysis and powers of implementation that may not exist. Hence, Lindblom and others argue for simplification by limiting policy analysis to those policies that differ in relatively small degree from policies presently in effect. Such a limitation immediately reduces the number of alternatives to be investigated, and also drastically simplifies the character of the investigation of each.

The practical application of such principles would produce health planning that is partial, not comprehensive; concerned with increments, not major reviews; with the organisation of existing services, not objectives and strategies for improving health status. Decision-makers would, according to this model, be concerned with means, and not with undefinable and unmeasurable goals. It is thus evident that incrementalism has been advanced primarily as a challenge to the rational model. It aspires to be not only a descriptive model, a realistic account of how things really are; but also a prescriptive model, of how things should be.

Incrementalism as a descriptive model has few opponents. Incrementalism as a prescriptive model has been challenged by those who, while accepting the shortcomings of the rational model, still consider it should represent an ideal to be attempted. Yet the incrementalist would argue that values and means are so closely intertwined, policy decisions involve so many different values, and conflicts over values are so widespread, that all decisions about public programmes are saturated with value choices. Where there is such complexity in the decision-making environment, the 'rational' approach to planning is unlikely to be feasible. Moreover, the theory of incrementalism is rooted in a belief that choice, in practice, is very limited. There is little point in generating and formulating strategies when the political and economic resources to sustain and implement them do not exist. Neither revolution, nor drastic policy change, nor even carefully planned large steps away from the status quo are ordinarily possible.[14] Reform has to take place on a piecemeal basis and the consequences of such reform will then be handled in a similar fashion.

The essence of incrementalism is 'partisan mutual adjustment', the conscious antithesis of rational planning. Planning becomes an institutionalised bargaining system, seeking to involve the multifarious interests of the relevant parties. The decisions reached will, in consequence, reflect the bargains struck or understandings reached between groups and the dominance of some interests and values over others.

However, as one recent writer [15] correctly notes, the theory needs considerable development to test its applicability to the social planning context. Who are the 'partisans'? How does one identify them and their interests? Do they have an explicit bargaining agenda? How are bargains arrived at? What is the currency? How is it traded? Is it possible to identify how much is given up by whom to gain what? What impact does the introduction of, or changes in, the rules of the game make? What factors inhibit adjustments and what promote them, and in whose interests are decisions made?

Later chapters will address a number of these questions, though it is important to record here that health planning will likely affect a variety of interests: hospital trustees, health administrators, medical care professionals, trade unions, third party payers, consumers and politicians. Most of these have their own goals to realise, and autonomy to protect.[16]

In the health sector, the most extreme of the incrementalist approaches is likely to occur where providers have considerable power and autonomy. In such circumstances, the shared interests of the providers in maintaining the status quo are likely to outweigh the differences that may separate them, and any disagreement will be controlled and limited. Thus, any explanation of the preservation of the status quo will need to concentrate on the ways in which the medical profession can exercise influence on the interpretation and implementation of decisions, and make even incremental moves difficult and infrequent.

For instance, several studies have suggested that, in the formative years of the NHS in England, medical consultants in the prestigious acute specialties dominated the local decision-making process; and that, ever since, incremental decision-making has permitted a policy drift towards high-technology medicine.[17] Historically, it would also appear that the actions of most local authorities in England are best described by the incremental model. The pattern of service provision has changed little from one year to the next, and only a small proportion of expenditures has been reviewed at any one time.[18] In short, plans focused on the development of existing services, to meet needs already acknowledged.

Similarly, studies in the USA indicate that health policy-makers and planners may be operating under a de facto incremental model, despite attempts to plan the health system under laws such as Comprehensive Health Planning, Regional Medical Programs and the more recent National Health Planning and Resources Development Act (see Chapter 2). As commentators have noted, these programmes may improve the information available to decision-makers, but they do not necessarily change the pattern of decision-making.

But what of the future? According to Klein[19], during periods of economic growth, governments tend to pursue policies that will allow Ministers to claim credit for improvements in health services; whereas, in periods of financial stringency, governments will tend to pursue policies of blame diffusion, to minimise their own task and to emphasise the importance of local decision-making. Whether this will lead to greater rationalism or greater incrementalism is an issue considered in Chapter 9.

Whatever the future may hold, in a number of countries the incremental model has offered a plausible explanation of how health policy-making and planning has been conducted in the past, though without fully indicating all the ways in which decision-making is limited and controlled by various interests. The problem is, should incrementalism become the prescribed pattern of behaviour? On one reading, incrementalism is to be preferred not only as a realistic approach to policy-making, but also as a politically relevant approach. It can be argued that a particular feature of the democratic process is that policies change almost entirely through incremental adjustments and, indeed, that major changes may threaten the viability of democracy. In addition, incrementalism can be entirely defensible if the best strategy is to proceed step by step on what information is available, while avoiding any decision which would pre-empt the long term. Indeed, incremental and sequential policy changes, corrected and adjusted at each step, have long been recognised as a highly effective means of proceeding under conditions of uncertainty.

However, it is never entirely clear whether a particular policy is incremental or not; many decisions which might appear to be a series of incremental steps may amount to the implementation of a fundamental review and a major alteration to the status quo. Such decisions are necessarily different in nature and in kind from steps rooted in the marginal-adjustment approach.

The danger is that the gradual adjustment promoted by incrementalism may frustrate the capacity of society to recognise or tackle higher-level problems, where radical change may be the required response. But, if politics is the 'art of the possible', planners must necessarily be concerned with finding out what is acceptable to the people who wield power. Yet, if the results are the lowest common denominators of the possible courses of action, such an approach may fail to address major social problems and to challenge major power groupings.

To avoid such outcomes, it might be considered desirable to set some limits to the dispersion and fragmentation of decision-making. What is far from clear, in any society, is where such limits should lie.[20] Dispersion of the decision-making process, and by implication minimisation of the role of government, conflicts with a need generally acknowledged by people throughout a society to make certain decisions collectively. A more active approach to societal decision-making might require two sets of mechanisms; one for fundamental decisions, and the other for incremental steps. This is precisely what mixed scanning claims to provide.

6 MIXED SCANNING

Incrementalism certainly provides one way of dealing with health care issues, but it may be considered by many as too limiting as an 'ideal' strategy. Yet experience with more comprehensive approaches has not been encouraging. Is there anything 'better' to put in their place? The questions left unanswered by these two approaches are:

(1) how should decision-making be directed to those strategic issues critical to the future of the organisation?

(2) how should the decision-maker arrive at and take those decisions, as systematically as possible, and with the most relevant information?

The aim of this section is not to sharpen the differences between the incremental and rational approaches, but rather to move towards an accommodation between these polar extremes.

The mixed scanning model, which falls somewhere in the middle of the decision-making model continuum, does incorporate elements of both the extremes. It emphasises the scanning of a number of possibilities from which are generated a selection of alternatives for action. Etzioni[21], who coined the term 'mixed scanning', indicates that such a strategy would employ two cameras: a wide-angled camera that would cover all parts of the landscape but not in great detail; and a second one which would zoom in on those areas indicated by the first camera as worthy of a more in-depth examination.

Hence, by using mixed scanning, the planner should not miss any major piece of data or feasible course of action, while not needing to consider all alternatives or undertake the in-depth assessment suggested by the rational strategy. In effect, decisions would be made incrementally but within the framework set by a broad analysis of basic assumptions and fundamental choices.

How might this operate in the health sector? A mixed scanning approach might embody three key components: a review process; a selection procedure; and then the detailed planning of major health issues.[22] In the first place, a scanning or review would be undertaken periodically to learn what has been happening in the health sector; to identify, and where possible anticipate, major issues for possible detailed attention; and, in general, to provide an overview on the basis of which future directions could be considered. The review process would consider the health sector in broad terms only, and would not attempt to produce detailed policies or plans. Second, the selection procedure would decide which of the issues identified were of fundamental importance and justified detailed planning, given the limited planning resources and skills likely to be available. Finally, the detailed planning of selected major issues would follow.

In essence, mixed scanning is consciously selective, accepts certain political and value assumptions and, by surveying the whole area of health policy, facilitates the identification of major issues which require in-depth analysis. Mixed scanning also highlights the inadequacies of the other two models of policy-making. It is more 'rational' in practice to be selective and systematic about a limited number of feasible options than 'rationally' to examine all the choices. Specifically, the criticism that rational planning is impossible, because complete comprehensiveness is impossible, is resolved by the concept of limited or bounded rationality, where only some alternatives and some consequences are related to some objectives. Yet mixed scanning does, in contrast to incrementalism, provide the opportunity for a more systematic, conscious approach to the identification and resolution of planning issues, which goes beyond merely reacting to problems as they emerge.

However, there is a difficulty. The theory as such does not tell us at what point selection ceases to be rational. Selectivity does require those issues to be identified that need detailed planning attention, but who should identify them, and what criteria should they apply? The experience of the United States in the 1960s and the UK in the 1970s showed that programme budgeting did not necessarily demand that each programme element should be subjected to an annual zero-based review; rather, it revealed that too little attention had been given by its designers to the criteria for 'selection' of planning issues.

Clearly, this is not a new problem; decisions about selection have always been faced by managers at all levels in the health sector for, with limited resources, only a certain number of issues can be tackled. What is new is the realisation that explicit criteria are needed to judge the suitability of a planning issue for major attention, as well as to decide which are best left to be dealt with internally within the appropriate organisation or department. Wiseman [23] offers a set of criteria, clustered under four headings, as follows: size of the issue; nature of the issue; future implications; and the political setting of the issue.

In the first place, the significance of an issue is often related to the magnitude of the resources committed to it, both in terms of quantity and quality. In addition, areas where resource commitments are changing rapidly may merit detailed consideration. Second, attention is likely to be given most profitably to those issues where choices on future developments are not tightly constrained, where there exists a large degree of discretion, and where choices are particularly complex or contentious. Third, from the planning point of view, those problems which, if tackled, are most likely to lead to future improvements in health need to be identified. Finally, while the level of urgency should influence selection, urgency is a matter of judgement and opinion; those involved in an advocacy role will inevitably regard the issue as of pressing concern. So the selection of an issue which might lead to a change in a policy where vested interests are at stake will have to take into account the likely political costs involved.

In short: the mixed scanning approach demands a set of

criteria for selecting planning issues which is both systematic and yet retains political realism. Indeed, the success of mixed scanning will depend not only upon the ability of all the major actors to be, at the same time, systematic and selective, but also upon the interaction between planning, the organisational structure and power relationships both within the medical care system and in the broader health sector.

7 INCENTIVE STRUCTURES AND PROSPECTS FOR CHANGE

Any national or regional health planning system will wish to avoid promoting policies and plans that run a high risk of failure by cutting across the grain of the organisations on which they are centred. Therefore, in making health plans that directly affect local populations and agencies, attention must be given to incentives, political processes and administrative organisations. Failure to implement plans can be described as:

(1) negative, where inadequate account is taken of personal interests that run counter to long-term organisational objectives; or

(2) positive, where inadequate attention is given to providing a set of incentives to channel the activities of managers and providers towards planning objectives.

If planning is to extend beyond the production of a plan, read and then forgotten, it is important to investigate and experiment with the use of incentives to increase the probability of implementation. A full consideration of this issue is deferred to the next chapter. Here, it needs to be mentioned that the policy-maker may have an incentive to devise policies which impose costs in a covert or hidden fashion, or which spread them widely over numerous people so that the incidence on any one individual or group is not substantial. For the same reason, the policy-maker may have a strong incentive to postpone or delay decisions which levy costs on powerful groups; in some cases, permanent postponement may be optimal from his point of view.[24]

What sanctions then exist to ensure that those in the health sector execute their duties, carry out agreed plans, and conform to budgets and other financial requirements? More positively, what inducements or encouragements are, or could be, provided – particularly when, in practice, disciplinary procedures may not be enforceable?[25] This is soft ground, more fertile in hypotheses than in final conclusions. For one thing, the reconciliation of individual interests with social welfare is not automatic. There is no guarantee that the considerable discretion enjoyed nationally by politicians and government officials, and locally by administrators, will be used in the best interests, where these can be established, of the general public; nor that medical influence will always be exerted in ways beneficial to the consumer, given that clinical staff are seldom accountable to the public for the services they provide.

There is evidence, however, in both Western Europe and North America, that cost containment, for instance, can be achieved, by the appropriate use of incentives and penalties, without adversely affecting the quality of care or the range of services offered. Further investigation is needed of what might be a suitable incentive structure to call forth the appropriate behaviour required for the implementation of health plans.

8 SUMMARY AND CONCLUSION

Several questions can be asked of planning and policy-making: does incrementalism rule the day; are policies the product of ad hoc decisions or of systematic planning; can planning be a rational and comprehensive activity; what critical factors govern the feasibility of health planning at various levels in a country?

One crucial factor has been seen to be the practicality or feasibility of reconciling conflicting goals, values and interests. It is possible that such reconciliation might be easier at higher levels in the hierarchy, where sectional interests, in terms of who gains and who loses resources, may not be so readily exhibited. At the national level, the concern of interest groups may be broader; if so, the possibilities for bargaining and compromise among these groups will be greater. A possible hypothesis for testing might, therefore, be that defensive behaviour and conflicts of interest are inherently greater at the local level where health services are provided. Moreover, while governments can often alter, directly or indirectly, the flow of funds into the health care system, the effective translation of plans into a set of actions will depend upon the behaviour of individuals and groups in specific locations. Group interests are thus more evidently promoted or challenged at the local level.

Must planning, therefore, be simply a tool which keeps political conflicts and change to the minimum?[26] Or does planning depend upon recognising, but not overestimating, political constraints in the selection of issues to be examined and alternatives to be considered? If the second interpretation is the more accurate, the question is not how planning can supplant the political process but whether and how it can fit into that process. Although planning does not, and cannot, seek to replace the political decision-making process it will, if successful, modify that process. And, equally, to be successful it must adapt to the political realities of decision-making.

Advocates of the pure form of rational planning have said that all conceivable courses of action must be identified and evaluated against all relevant ends. Thus, they urge that all planning must proceed comprehensively. Against this the critics of such an approach consider it neither possible nor desirable to perform such a comprehensive review and analysis. Rather, the science of incrementalism emphasises only marginal changes in policy, thus drastically reducing the number and complexity of policy alternatives. The major difference between the rationalist theories and incrementalism has been seen to be that the former base their theories on maximising the attainment of goals, while the incrementalists argue that decision-makers do (and should) concentrate on means, not goals.

In conclusion, it seems probable that observable instances of planning are likely to fall somewhere between these two extremes, though weighted more towards incrementalism than rationalism. Nevertheless, there is scope for analytical approaches which can help to clarify the nature of any political judgement, by systematically setting out information on the possible effects of such decisions and by making assumptions and uncertainties explicit. What is unclear is whether mixed scanning will prove acceptable to decision-makers. Politically and intellectually it may be more painful than 'muddling through', and for that reason may be immediately unattractive.

NOTES

1. M. Carley, 'Rational Techniques in Policy Analysis' (Heinemann, London, 1980).
2. M. Shani, Futures Studies Versus Planning, 'Omega', vol. 2, no. 5 (1974).
3. A. Faludi (ed.), 'A Reader in Planning Theory' (Pergamon Press, Oxford, 1973); and A. Faludi, 'Planning Theory' (Pergamon Press, Oxford, 1973).
4. D. E. Berry, The Transfer of Planning Theories to Health Planning Practice, 'Policy Sciences', vol. 5 (1974).
5. G. Lind and C. Wiseman, Setting Health Priorities: a Review of Concepts and Approaches, 'Journal of Social Policy', vol. 7, no. 4 (1978), pp. 411-40.
6. K. Lee, Health Care: Planning, Policies and Incentives, 'Futures', vol. 11, no. 6 (1979), pp. 482-90.
7. D. Allen, 'Hospital Planning' (Pitman Medical, Tunbridge Wells, 1979).
8. R. Klein, Policy Problems and Policy Perceptions in the National Health Service, 'Policy and Politics', vol. 2, no. 3 (1974).
9. A.-M. Foltz, M. Chen and A. Stoga, Public Policy and Health Resource Distribution, 'Policy Sciences', vol. 8 (1977), pp. 323-41.

10. K. Lee, Public Expenditure, Planning and Local Democracy in K. Barnard and K. Lee (eds.), 'Conflicts in the National Health Service' (Croom Helm, London, and Prodist, New York, 1977).
11. WHO, 'Guiding Principles for the Managerial Process for National Health Development' (WHO, Geneva, September 1980).
12. E. C. Banfield, Ends and Means in Planning, 'International Social Science Journal', vol. XI, no. 3 (1959), and reprinted in Faludi, 'A Reader in Planning Theory'.
13. C. E. Lindblom, The Science of 'Muddling Through', 'Public Administration Review' (Spring 1959), also reprinted in Faludi, 'A Reader in Planning Theory'.
14. C. E. Lindblom, Still Muddling, Not Yet Through, 'Public Administration Review' (November/December 1979), pp. 517-26.
15. H. Glennerster, From Containment to Conflict? - Social Planning in the Seventies, 'Journal of Social Policy', vol. 10, no. 1 (1981), pp. 31-51.
16. T. R. Marmor and A. Bridges, American Health Planning and the Lessons of Comparative Policy Analysis, 'Journal of Health Politics, Policy and Law', vol. 5, no. 3 (Fall 1980), pp. 419-30.
17. A. Alaszewski, P. Tether and H. McDonnell, Another Dose of Managerialism? - Commentary on the Consultative Paper 'Patients First', 'Social Science and Medicine', vol. 15A (1981), pp. 3-15.
18. A. Booth (ed.), 'Planning for Welfare: Social Policy and the Expenditure Process' (Basil Blackwell and Martin Robertson, Oxford, 1979).
19. R. Klein, The Strategy behind the Jenkin Non-Strategy, 'British Medical Journal', 28 March 1981, pp. 1089-91.
20. K. Lee, Public Expenditure, Health Services, and Health in A. Walker (ed.), 'Public Expenditure and Social Priorities' (Heinemann, London, 1981).
21. A. Etzioni, Mixed Scanning: a 'Third' Approach to Decision-Making, 'Public Administration Review' (December 1967).
22. C. Wiseman, 'Strategic Planning in the Scottish Health Service - a Mixed-Scanning Approach' (Institute for Operational Research, Tavistock Institute of Human Relations, June 1977).
23. C. Wiseman, Selection of Major Planning Issues, 'Policy Sciences', vol. 9 (1978), pp. 71-86.
24. R. H. Haveman, Policy Analysis and the Congress: an Economist's View, in R. H. Haveman and J. Margolis, 'Public Expenditure and Policy Analysis', 2nd edn (Rand McNally College Pub. Co., Chicago, 1977), reprinted from 'Policy Analysis', vol. 2, no. 2, (Spring 1976), pp. 235-50.

25. B. Abel-Smith and A. Leiserson, Poverty, Development, and Health Policy, 'Public Health Paper 69' (WHO, Geneva, 1978).
26. T. Sudama, PPBS and Theories of Decision-Making, Bureaucracy and Politics, 'Public Finance', vol. 32, no. 3 (1977), pp. 354-73.

1   INTRODUCTION

Over the last thirty years, sustained economic growth has been accompanied by greater public expenditure in the area of social welfare. This overall growth in the welfare role of the state is certainly common to all Western industrialised countries, despite their very different histories and political complexions. Specifically, the state has become a dominant, or at least a major, provider of services such as education, health care and social security, towards which an increasingly wealthy society has shifted its consumption preferences.[1]

As a consequence, it might have been expected that these developments would have prompted a searching inquiry into the organisational structure and behaviour of agencies in the public sector, and into government and agency relationships. Seemingly, however, there has been little empirical research into these issues and, hence, there is little agreement about such crucial questions as who makes the resource allocation decisions; what are the objectives of the decision-makers; and what type of model is most appropriate for the study of policy-making and policy implementation. This chapter proposes to make a start in this area, by examining the individual and corporate objectives and motives which may underpin much of present-day behaviour of public agencies in the health sector.

Once it is accepted, as discussed in earlier chapters, that there is a multiplicity of decision-making groups in each health agency, and limits on the ability of any one individual or group to impose its will on others, then it is no longer immediately obvious what meaning to attach to what are commonly called the 'objectives' of the agency. The significance of this conclusion for health policy and planning is that it focuses attention on the health agencies themselves, and on their organisation, objectives and behaviour. What limits their power if they are not dependent on market forces, and what are the ultimate determinants, internal and external, of their performance? If profit maximisation is not essential, then what alternative motivations exist? There are no generally agreed answers to such questions, though there is an extensive literature devoted to various managerial and organisational theories of the firm. Much of this literature acknowledges that profit may not be a firm's central objective. Indeed, in the health sector, management may not be at all profit-responsible;

and this feature may well widen further the scope of managerial discretion.

Is it at all possible, therefore, to view private commercial firms and health agencies as enjoying certain common features? Both types of organisation are responsible to ultimate decision-makers (shareholders and governments); but there is a degree of imprecision about their objectives which allows latitude to those managing, and working within, them. At the very least, this suggests that, in analysing the behaviour of public agencies in the health sector, it should be possible to draw on parallels with the theory of the firm. This task is undertaken in section 2 of this chapter.

One of the difficulties of conducting such an analysis is determining who is making what decisions, and what goals each person or group is pursuing. Politicians or, more precisely, those who belong to the ruling party or coalition, will be involved in decision-making, especially about financial resources. Public officials, whether civil servants, trustees or managers, also influence greatly a range of decisions over resources, both independently and in conjunction with politicians, and cannot be assumed simply to be able people passively carrying out the orders of politicians. Employees, whether as individuals or as members of professional associations and trade unions, can be expected to help shape decision-making, at central as well as at a more local level. Finally, one can turn to the general public who, in two guises, might participate in decision-making and influence the resource rationing process. First, there is the voter who has a positive but indirect effect upon resource distribution by his voting behaviour; and second, there is the consumer/client/patient who has a more direct personal involvement in the rationing process, though his role is often conceived to be an entirely passive one. Section 3 considers the goals of some of these groups and the way(s) in which each might influence decision-making in the health sector.[2]

A major factor remaining to be considered is the practicality or feasibility of reconciling the conflicting goals, values and interests of these various groups and individuals. Hence, alternative models of how differing preferences are reconciled to reach decisions are considered in section 4. The relevant explanatory model can reasonably be expected to differ from situation to situation.

Finally, it is probable that there exist quite different decision-making and information structures, a priori restrictions and incentive structures both between and within countries. The recognition of these differences is essential to an analysis of policy-making and planning within the health sector. Hence, the overall intention of this chapter is to lead into an analysis of what might be happening in public agencies within the health sector, and why; and, thereby, to consider the implications for future policy determination.

2 SOME THEORIES OF THE FIRM

Introduction

The assumption of profit maximisation as the objective of the firm is one of the cornerstones of traditional economic theory. However, if this assumption is relaxed to take into account two important factors - that the owners of the firm are separate from those managing and controlling it, and that firms operate in an economic environment which affords their managers an element of discretion over the firm's goals - then the behaviour of the firm will depend to some extent on the objective(s) of those running it. In principle, it can be argued that these same two factors apply to public agencies in the health sector.

In the private sector, conventional economic analysis has had to come up with explanations which give a more accurate picture of the real behaviour of business firms than does a theory founded on profit maximisation. Two alternative sets of theories have been proposed to account for actual behaviour. The first set, under the broad heading of managerial theories, all assume that the managers are maximisers, but differ in terms of which variables they are thought to seek to maximise. These theories, therefore, retain the maximisation of stated objectives as the underlying assumption, but since the objective is not profits (nor directly profit-related), the firms can pursue other objectives (subject to constraints).

In contrast, behavioural theories of the firm relax the maximisation postulate, replacing it by the idea of satisficing, a hybrid word suggesting that common business behaviour falls somewhere between that which entirely satisfies and that which merely suffices. Central to the approach of this school (of organisational theorists) is the thesis that the problems of internal co-ordination and decision-making are so immense that the assumption of an objective to be maximised is inappropriate and must be replaced by the assumption of a number of 'acceptable-level' goals to be 'satisficed'.

In summary: managerial theorists build up the objectives of the firm by a consideration of the objectives, aims and drives of the various individuals (and groups) within the firm but arrive at an objective which is then maximised; whereas behavioural theorists argue that if the firm is seen as a coalition of groups with conflicting interests then the notion of maximisation is inappropriate. What then are their arguments and differences in detail?

Managerial (Maximising) Theories

(1) <u>Profit Maximisation</u>. The theory of supply in a competitive free-enterprise economy is well developed. In its purest form, the firm is identified with the entrepreneur, the owner-

manager who takes the risks, makes the decisions and receives the rewards. The entrepreneur, in turn, is assumed to be 'economic man', interested solely in maximising his utility by maximising his profits. Since the entrepreneur is in complete control, the maximisation of his profits becomes the objective or goal of the firm. Furthermore, in competitive markets, profit maximisation is a condition of survival, since only those firms which make profits survive.[3] Only when ownership is separated from control, or when government ownership replaces private ownership, is this internal decision-making process affected. If, at the same time, market competition is lax or impeded, then changes in the incentive structure of the entire organisation, and in the motivations of those working within and for it, may occur. Together, these factors are likely to have important implications for both the quality of the good or service produced, and for the efficiency of the production process.[4]

(2) Sales Maximisation. The theory of Baumol [5] has as its main theme the view that managers seek to maximise sales revenue of the firm, subject to earning an 'acceptable' level of profits for the firm. Beyond this acceptable level, acceptable that is to the owners, further increases in profit can be sacrificed if this permits increased sales revenue. A wide range of reasons has been put forward for believing that the firm will maximise sales. Baumol argues that since many managers' salaries appear to be more closely linked to sales than to profits, personal self-interest will lead them to promote sales. Also, their promotion prospects and standing in the firm may be judged, by the owners, in terms of sales. The inference to be drawn is that the owners are also sales maximisers, or at least acquiesce with - or condone - such behaviour. Though the sales maximisation hypothesis is related to cash and not volume sales, when applied within the health agency context there are reasons for suggesting that both government officials and managers benefit from the equivalent of sales, namely increased throughput/workload, albeit for different reasons.

(3) Growth Maximisation. The theory of Marris [6] has three parts: a view about the manager's motivations and how these motives are made operational within the firm; a view of how the stock market values the firm; and a theory of take-overs, with the threat of a take-over being the main constraint on managers' behaviour. Given that the prospect of take-overs and the influence of the stock market are not concerns for any but proprietary health agencies, the relevance of the theory to most health agencies rests solely on its treatment of motivation. On this point, the theory suggests that the ambitions of the managers, for income, status and power, lead the firm to maximise a utility function concerned with growth but coupled with security.

(4) Maximising Managerial Discretion. The model of William-

son[7] can be seen as an elaboration of the models already presented, though it does contain differences of emphasis. The goals of the firm, subject to reported profit exceeding some minimum acceptable level, are constructed out of the immediate objectives of its managers. The manager's utility function is a function of the number and quality of staff employed, the rewards of management and 'discretionary' profits. The number of people on a manager's staff and their professional qualifications and competence give the manager prestige and power, and make promotion prospects more favourable for himself and his staff. The rewards of management may be direct financial payments (income, bonuses), or may take the form of indirect income (perquisites such as company cars, expense accounts, spacious offices). Finally, 'discretionary' profits are those profits made above the minimum profit constraint which afford the manager a degree of latitude (i.e. discretion) in allocating the resources and investments of the firm. Depending upon the economic environment faced by the firm, managers may have considerable room for manoeuvre. In such circumstances, the important determinants of managerial behaviour are argued to be salary, status, power, prestige and security.

Behavioural (Satisficing) Theories

The managerial theories considered above are all based on the idea that firms do not consider profit maximisation to be the prime objective. The behavioural theories abandon also the view that firms are maximisers. It is important to explore why they adopt this stance. One of the immediately striking features of the firm as a large organisation is that it is difficult to talk with any sense about its objectives.[8] Rather, the firm appears to behave as a 'coalition' of individuals and groups of individuals with conflicting interests. Individuals and groups within the firm can still be assumed to have their own objectives, and hence it is possible to talk of them seeking to maximise their own objectives. But it is probable that maximisation attempts by any one group would only heighten the conflict with other groups, such that full maximisation by one group is unlikely to be feasible.

This line of thought has led some theorists to replace the idea of maximisation with the notion of 'satisficing'; Simon [9] and Cyert and March[10], in particular, are associated with this school of thought. They argue that, in many cases, management recognises implicitly or explicitly the complexities of the calculations and the imperfections of the data which must be employed in any optimality calculation. As a result, firms frequently give up the attempt to maximise anything – sales, profits or whatever. Instead they set for themselves some minimum standards of achievement which they hope will assure the firm's viability.

Simon, and Cyert and March argue that organisational goals are formed by a process of bargaining between the members of the 'coalition'. Explicitly or implicitly, a process of bargaining occurs continuously, in which 'side payments', such as salaries or commitments to particular lines of business or specific policies, are made in order to induce others to join a particular coalition. The objectives of such 'inducements' are to encourage individuals and groups to join the firm and stay in it, to pursue particular activities, and to agree to particular policies favoured by others.

How are conflicts dealt with? The organisation is able to survive with conflicting goals partly because some of the objectives are expressed in non-operational terms; partly because at any point of time all objectives will not be pursued; but mainly because objectives will be considered sequentially and not simultaneously. The consequence is that inefficiencies, or 'organisational slack' as it is termed, will arise directly from the bargaining and decision process.

Summary

As noted above, among the suggested alternatives to setting profit maximisation as the objective of the firm are Baumol's sales maximisation subject to a profit constraint, Marris's growth maximisation subject to a security constraint, and Williamson's maximisation of a generalised managerial utility function subject to a profit constraint. The motives that have, thereby, been attributed to management include income, status and power, comfort and security, though there is disagreement as to the relative importance of each. Likewise, there is less than total agreement about the objectives to which these motives give rise, though where profit is not selected as the prime objective, some form of profit consideration is always retained, especially as a long-run constraint. There is a good deal of agreement[11], however, that growth is likely to be a central objective. This view, as will be considered later, may be of particular significance when applied to public agencies in the health sector.

In contrast to these managerial theories, the 'behavioural' school stresses that the various groups within a large organisation are not cohesive, that the many functions of management are likely to generate important divisions between managers, and that maximisation is not a likely outcome. Rather, divisive elements are consciously minimised by aiming for a satisfactory 'aspiration' level, by taking decisions sequentially, and by allowing organisational slack to persist.

In summary, managerial theories build up the objectives of the firm by a consideration of the utility-maximising behaviour of the key individuals within the firm, whereas behavioural theories relax the maximisation hypothesis and replace it with the concept of satisficing, whereby firms seek satisfactory levels of performance in certain key variables such as profits, sales and growth. Before, however, jumping to the conclusion that any organisational 'slack' that may exist is a consequence of organisational conflict (satisficing) rather than a desired objective of managers (maximising), further consideration of each actor's objectives and behaviour is necessary. This is considered in the next section.

3 ACTORS IN THE DECISION-MAKING PROCESS

Introduction

This section reviews some of the theoretical work done in recent years to develop theories and models of decision-making in the public sector, and attempts to apply them, where possible, to public agencies in the health sector. The format that follows is designed in order to consider each group of actors separately; the interaction between groups of actors is the subject of section 4.

Governments and Ministers

(1) <u>Governments</u>. Few would deny that, in a democracy, the electoral system and voting patterns are important to politicians in general, and to governments in particular, and thus ought to enter into a model of government behaviour:

> Politicians may, and indeed many do, seek to serve the wider national interest by introducing sweeping social reforms. But they will never be able to do so unless they get elected to office, and to get elected to office it is necessary to adopt those policies that will win votes.[12]

It has, therefore, been posited that vote maximisation (or minimisation of the votes of the opposition) represents a more accurate view of politicians' objectives than does the assumption that they pursue an idealised notion of the 'national interest', however this might be defined. But what are the other important arguments in a political party's utility function? Assuming that political parties are first motivated to win (or not to lose) votes, governments may still pursue other objectives, such as power, prestige, perquisites, altruism, patronage and personal incomes, albeit with an eye always on the future and the need to be re-elected.

Various theories, all of which run the danger of over-simplification, have been developed. One view might be that the political party in power - whether at the national or local level - will dispense public funds (such as the health budget) on the basis of 'patronage', and spend in those geographical localities voting predominantly in support of the party in power. Hence, public spending would be proportional to majority strength. A second view, analysed in detail by Downs[13], maintains that political parties, in choosing, for example, health policies, have to appeal to the 'centre' of the political spectrum, if a majority vote is to be gained. In time, these policies may well coalesce, so that the programmes advanced by all the leading parties within a country will simply mirror the wishes of the 'median voter'.

The third view partly borrows and partly challenges the first two analyses. It offers a model of vote-buying through budgeting which assumes that public funds will be spent where the power obtained per dollar spent is highest.[14] This will not be in localities with 'safe' seats since votes there are - if not superfluous - at least less valuable in political terms than votes in more closely contested constituencies. Nor will it be in electoral districts where the chance of winning an additional seat is remote. If spending on health services in a district can 'buy votes', then the model would lead to the prediction that more money will be spent where the votes won are most valuable, in terms of producing another seat.

It remains to be fully tested whether public spending decisions on health and health services, by central and/or local government, are influenced by such political motives; or whether, as one suspects, the view of political parties as purely organisations for winning political power is too simplistic. A possible sophistication of the models could consider whether parties might not reject vote maximisation in favour of the achievement of a 'satisfactory' number of votes to get elected. However, whether such behaviour would accord with 'satisficing' or with 'maximising discretion' merits further analysis.

(2) Ministers. As a starting-point, it can be assumed that a politician is motivated to seek Ministerial office for reasons other than, or in addition to, simply representing the views of his electorate. While altruism in the public sector undoubtedly exists, the question must be asked what importance it has in the Minister's utility function: 'The old notion that politicians and bureaucrats are dedicated to the common good that is unrelated to their own interest is not a good ground on which to build a theory of the working of politics.'[15] Alongside the development of a theory of government behaviour, therefore, efforts need to be directed to analysing the behaviour of Ministers. They are likely to be no different from the general population in wishing to maximise their own utility function; but what is unclear are the important factors in that function.

If one concentrates attention here upon the ultimate authority for government health expenditure, i.e. who is formally accountable for how the funds are used, then the appropriate person is the Minister of Health. According to one source: 'If I had to guess at the components in the Minister's utility function, I would say that he "trades off" political

66

ambition within the Government against the perceived benefits to him of party loyalty.'[16] A Minister might be motivated to maximise his departmental budget as a condition for achieving the first of these ends. Clearly, more expenditure might offer him more scope and control over a wider range of activities associated with his Ministry; whereas altering the composition rather than the amount of the budget may have too high an opportunity cost in terms of dissent within his own Ministry.

However, Cabinet solidarity (or party loyalty) may act as a firm constraint upon the pursuit of budget maximisation, to the extent that under certain circumstances, a Minister's political ambitions may be more easily realised by 'pruning' his budget. The costs to the government of the day of granting an increased budget to health are the alternative uses of the receipts; in terms of the ultimate aim of retaining power, few health services are not substitutable, at the margin, for other public services, or for reduced public expenditure.

This potential conflict between personal ambitions and the aims of the government is even more acute when account is taken of the Minister of Health's responsibilities to his own department. But a Minister also has responsibilities to his constituency and to his party, not to mention the Cabinet (in the UK). The question is thus whether, despite the fragmented nature of his obligations and loyalties, the centre of his existence is still his responsibilities as Minister. One ex-Minister has asserted that it is:

> I would suggest that a minister who from the most honourable of motives fights insufficiently hard, and becomes too impressed by the concept of 'Cabinet policy as a whole', may be storing up pretty desperate problems for his successor, his department, and even for his own Cabinet colleagues who later on have to sort out the mess. On balance I would still commend Churchill's advice to a new and inexperienced minister: 'You fight your corner'.[17]

Yet, even if a Minister accepts such advice and fights for his Ministry, he may still encounter difficulties in attempting to implement Ministerial policies. Health policies are 'mediated' through public agencies, including his own department, and the actors within them, such that the desired ends of the Minister may diverge from the objectives of actors at both the centre and the periphery.

Administrators

It is necessary, in consequence, to consider what it is that motivates administrators, whether civil servant, hospital administrator or social services director. The picture of the faceless administrator, obediently accepting orders from above, executing but not making policy choices, and motivated only to forward the 'public interest' appears unrealistic to many. For one thing, the definition of the 'public interest' is itself formed by the political process, and may be subject to varying interpretations. For another, administrators may be considered to resemble the rest of the population:

> to some extent interested in the public good and in helping their fellow men; but like the rest of us, they put far more time and attention into their private concerns. Thus the bureaucrat, in making a decision about some matter, is likely to give more weight to the effect of his decision on his personal career than on the nation as a whole.[18]

In consequence, administrators cannot be conceived as 'economic eunuchs'[19]; they are key members of the cast of public decision-makers. They are, in short, actors in the drama rather than stage managers. Hence, it is obligatory to look closely at bureaucratic/organisational structures and at individual behaviour within those structures. What then are the rewards and penalties facing an administrator located in a hierarchy, and what sorts of behaviour would characterise his efforts to maximise his utility?

The essence of the 'economics of bureaucracy' approach is that there is a close analogy between the theory of the firm and the theory of bureaucratic operation. Those who manage or administer a health agency inevitably possess information that they may choose not to make available to politicians, legislators or voters, thereby limiting the latter's ability to monitor accurately the performance of government agencies.[20] Likewise, although administrators may be precluded from maximising profits, and may not produce an output for direct sale, their sources of satisfaction may be regarded as similar to those who work in the private sector.[21] But do public officials differ in terms of which variables they are thought to seek to maximise?

(1) Maximising the Size of the Budget. Building on some of the earlier propositions put forward by Downs[22], especially his view of utility maximisation by bureaucrats and the elements (such as power, income, prestige, security) which generate utility, Niskanen [23] has suggested that bureaucrats maximise their utility by maximising the size of their budget, provided that total cost does not exceed total revenue (or a predetermined cost level). The power, income, prestige, etc. of bureaucrats are held to be directly related to the size of a bureau's budget; hence the bureaucrat's natural tendency will be to seek to increase the budget.

A number of factors have been identified as encouraging self-sustaining growth in health budgets.[24] In the first place, in some societies, salaries and perquisites of office are related directly to the size of the budgets administered and controlled. Second, expanding agencies tend to attract more capable personnel through their high rates of promotion. Third, rapid growth creates opportunities for all health officials, and minimises internal conflict for scarce resources. Finally, the larger the agency, the more stability it can impose on its environment, for instance by enforcing its preferences upon politicians and upon those for whom the service is provided.[25]

The budget-maximising administrator is, therefore, far from being a neutral agent in the decision-making process over resources. But how might this desire to maximise the health budget manifest itself? First, there may be a tendency among health officials to advocate either a low charge or no charge for health services, in order to encourage 'need' to show itself. This is particularly likely if officials perceive that the scale of provision is directly linked to their own status. Alternatively, administrators may seek to obtain agreement to expand a given health programme by systematically overstating the benefits or understating the costs. Third, in carrying out their own duties, they may be able either to 'control the agenda' by offering only a limited choice of health expenditure programmes from which to choose,[26] or to manipulate the details of health policy so as to increase the demands for, and the rewards paid to, themselves. Similarly, health officials may not favour reductions in expenditure; in most cases, they may be more strongly opposed to 'cuts' than the population as a whole. Thus, even within a specified budget, there may be elements of discretion which allow the pattern of health expenditure to reflect officials' wishes rather than public preferences.

A conclusion of interest to health policy-makers is that, if all health officials were to act in the ways described, resources would be wasted. Whether they are able to act in that manner depends on the constraints they face, and on what methods exist to improve bureaucratic efficiency. A crucial factor is the relationship between health officials and government. This may be likened to one of bilateral monopoly, in which the construction of plans and the implementation of policies depend upon the distribution of power and influence between the two parties in the exchange. In this context, widening the scope of competition for funds between health agencies[27], altering the rewards system for officials (such as efficiency bonuses for top administrators) or facilitating investigations of health Ministries and health agencies by 'watchdog' committees may all inhibit any tendency for administrators to operate in a fully monopolistic situation.[28]

(2) Quality Maximising Models. The next model to be considered, that of M. L. Lee[29], considers the motives of administrators at hospital level, and places emphasis on the quality of care provided. The context is US medical care, and the assumption made is that a number of variables in the

hospital administrator's utility function - salary, prestige, security, power, professional satisfaction among others - are all dependent upon the status of the hospital. Thus, it is assumed that the administrator's drive for status plays a dominant role in the behaviour of the hospital.

Lee's basic hypothesis is that a hospital administrator will attempt to minimise what he perceives to be the gap between the hospital's desired status and its actual status by 'purchasing' inputs normally to be found only in hospitals of higher status. Thus, the status of a hospital is assumed to vary directly with the range of services provided, and the extent to which expensive and highly specialised equipment and personnel are available.

The major consequences of the model may be summarised in both qualitative and quantitative terms. Qualitatively, 'conspicuous production' would result in the use of inputs beyond those warranted by production requirements. Highly trained personnel would be employed to perform tasks suitable for persons with less training, and equipment of advanced and complex design would be used for tasks not requiring such sophistication. Quantitatively, conspicuous production would result in undue duplication, over-equipment and over-staffing. In short: equipment, facilities and staff will be under-utilised, and what the hospital is equipped to produce may be quite different from its actual output.

Questions may, however, be raised about the assumptions underlying the model. In the first place, it represents an administrator's utility-maximising model, and other groups, such as doctors, are viewed as either accepting or supporting the status-maximising objective. It follows that, if a group other than hospital administrators acts as a countervailing force, then this must be taken account of in the model. Thus the model may suffer from a lack of completeness. Furthermore, the model's underlying insight is that administrators seek prestige, and in order to do this they transform 'their' organisation into a prestigious one through 'input' changes. However, if prestige and status are not judged sólely in terms of inputs (i.e. resources), then the model is again incomplete in ignoring what actually happens in the hospital, the characteristics of its output, and how these are perceived by various interested parties.

(3) Quantity-Quality Maximising Models. The third group covers models that suggest that the administrator has a utility function that includes some measure of the quality of the health agency as well as the size of its budget. For example, in Newhouse's model [30] of the hospital, the decision-maker is a monolithic amalgam of trustees, doctors and hospital administrators, which seeks to maximise a weighted function of quality and quantity. All three groups are assumed to have stakes in both variables and by some form of bargaining process achieve a 'final resolution' among their tastes, so that

it becomes possible to speak of maximising the 'tastes' of the hospital decision-maker.

The model assumes that the hospital's decision-maker will seek to maximise the utility function either in terms of increased quantity - increased capacity, or facilities and services that result in an increase in patient numbers - or in prestige/quality inputs.[31] Yet quality and quantity cannot be maximised without limit. The non-profit agency is faced by a budget constraint: its deficit cannot be larger than a certain amount; its cash allocation may be fixed in advance.

Perhaps the major issue posed by Newhouse's model is whether or not the hospital can be modelled in terms of a 'firm' with a single head with a single utility function.[32] In defence, Newhouse accepts that administrators, trustees and medical staff may weight quality and quantity considerations differently, even if the elements in their respective utility functions can be assumed to be the same. But this need not impair the theory. Empirically, the question is still one of whether a single maximand - based on quality and quantity - can be derived by observing the self-interests of administrators, medical staff and others.

(4) Maximising Administrative Discretion. In general, the irrelevance of profit as the ultimate goal must strengthen the influence of other motives attributed to health administrators, and yet administrators cannot remain totally and systematically inefficient. However, the high visibility of public services may lead to what has been termed 'risk aversion' - efforts directed at avoiding 'mistakes':

> since it is large 'failures' that are easily detected and that, as a consequence, reap penalties, methods are sought to ensure that large risks that entail high probabilities of failure are not undertaken or, if undertaken, that responsibility does not rest on any single individual, for example by requiring consultation among a number of individuals.[33]

Risk aversion may be but one illustration of ways in which the administrator can promote his interests. Although Niskanen has argued that, in practice, managers have little choice and must employ their discretionary budget in only one way - to increase output - it is usually apparent that, in the government sector, output is only one consideration among many. Indeed, one could advance the proposition that bureaucrats and managers do not even attempt to maximise their budgets or their bureau's output. The basic idea behind the managerial discretion approach is that managers are assumed to derive personal satisfaction from allocating resources of their firm to other than productivity increasing expenses.[34] These resources can be used in a variety of ways, depending upon administrators' preferences, ranging from greater emoluments and power to greater office comforts. The question then becomes one of whether the administrator is seeking to maximise his utility function or whether he is adopting 'satisficing' behaviour. If the latter, this places a limit on the investment of time, energy and skill he would be willing to devote to it. In short: can discretionary behaviour become satisficing behaviour; or, possibly a better question, what combination of maximising and satisficing is to be found in practice?

Doctors

Human resources make up a very large proportion of the total resources allocated to the health sector. Thus, the varieties and mix of workers employed are likely to be prime determinants of the nature and extent of the health services provided:

> People, in spite of the application to them of the objectified term 'manpower', are not a passive resource, and have interests of their own which [may] conflict with those of the planners. These interests may relate to individuals, who might object to physical transfer, changes in working times or duties, or to groups, whether defined by profession, status, place in the organisation structure, or other characteristic.[35]

In consequence, although all the models already presented in this chapter shed light on the decision-making process and its outcome, at the micro level they may be said to suffer by not embracing the motivations of all health employees, professional or otherwise. For reasons of space, only one of these other groups of employees is considered below, namely the medical profession.

Doctors represent a group whose role in the allocation of resources and in decision-making is just as decisive as that of administrators in certain respects. Indeed, this may be an understatement; medicine holds the centre of the stage, for without the hero there would be no play. An analysis of decision-making perhaps should start with an account of the interaction of doctors, patients and resources; and of the degree of autonomy enjoyed by doctors in exercising their judgement.

One model of US hospitals, offered by Pauly and Redisch[36], has as its critical assumption that doctors enjoy de facto control of hospital activities and see to it that hospital services are produced in such a way as to maximise doctors' net incomes. In their model, hospital doctors have direct control over the number and types of patients admitted and over the types of services they receive; in other words, they control output. They determine, within rather broad limits, what use will be made of the hospital in treating a patient; they control many of the production decisions. They have indirect control over many other aspects of the hospital's operation, such as capital investment and the level of nursing care, in the sense that no administrator can afford to incur the displeasure of the medical staff, interfere with medical staff prerogatives, or make decisions which would deter large numbers of physicians from remaining on the hospital's staff or using that hospital for their patients. The trustees, who have nominal control over the hospital's budget, are said to merely 'legitimise the hospital to the local community'. It can be argued that in these circumstances, doctors will have no incentive to keep hospital costs down (indeed, they may well seek high-cost equipment and high staffing levels so that they can economise on their own time), and inefficiencies will result.

The main thrust of the model, and the feature that differentiates it from other models, is the assumption that doctors aim to maximise their income. However, this insistence on a sole variable in the utility function, namely income, has attracted critics. They argue that the model ignores non-monetary components of a doctor's income, such as leisure time and prestige, which may be considered to be of some importance, especially in those countries where doctors receive a fixed salary. In such instances, doctors may choose to concentrate on work they find most interesting; though their ability to do this may well be a function of the quantity and quality of the facilities available, since facilities determine in part doctors' own productivity and their perceived status.[37] Further, the model assumes that doctors will, at any point in time, act in such a way as to maximise the sum of the money incomes of their profession. Such an assumption implies a process of group decision-making which may not occur in practice. Finally, by concentrating solely on doctors' behaviour, the model conveniently ignores the participation of the administrator and others in the decision-making process.[38]

Nevertheless, this model is useful as a benchmark from which to consider those alternative hypotheses considered above, which do not rank 'income' so highly in the utility function. Certainly it would be unwise to underplay the influence doctors have, individually and collectively, in making resource allocation decisions and in shaping future policies. What is questionable, however, is whether the medical staff do, indeed, 'hold all the aces'. Doctors may be dominant, but the influence of other actors on planning and policy determination cannot be lightly dismissed.

4 DECISION-MAKING: MAXIMISING OR SATISFICING?

Introduction

As was discussed extensively in Chapter 3, so many individuals, groups and organisations are involved in decision-making in the health sector [39] that only by (happy) coincidence will individuals' preferences be in accord:

> If you are to argue that individuals have similar preferences, you are forced into a position where you must explain why. And if you can think of no good reason why they should do so, you are required to acknowledge that preferences may differ among persons.[40]

Accepting the logic of this argument, a major problem in the health sector is the practicality or feasibility of reconciling conflicting goals, values and interests. As no counterpart of the 'invisible hand' of competitive markets is present, the reconciliation of rival interests cannot be assumed to be automatic, and one should not expect a single 'social welfare function' to emerge. To illustrate this point, attention is focused below on the interactions between administrators and doctors, and then on those between trustees and administrators.

Administrators and Doctors

Many health agencies, such as hospitals, are characterised by a dual authority structure – an administrative structure organised bureaucratically, and a professional authority structure distinguished by professional autonomy. The presence of such a potential schism in the decision-making process will influence the process of resource allocation, and some economists have attempted to come to terms with this in one way or another.

The dominance of the medical profession over administrators, and the lack of influence of trustees, as assumed in the Pauly and Redisch model discussed above, is challenged in a paper by Harris.[41] In it, he observes that the medical staff and administrative staff each have their own objectives, decision variables and constraints, and that the hospital is actually two firms in one. Although this has been acknowledged before, it has been modelled in rather different ways. In some versions, doctors are regarded as independent entrepreneurs separate from the hospital. In others, they are assumed to be subordinate to administrators and trustees. In still others, doctors have de facto control over the organisation.

Harris criticises these models for not facing directly questions of conflict resolution and resource allocation within the hospital. If it is conceded that the hospital is two firms (doctor-firm and administrator-firm), then the question is how are their roles co-ordinated, given that each firm may well have its own objectives and constraints. The answer, according to Harris, is that internal order is achieved not by strategic planning, but through incremental adjustments. Hence, the hospital solves its problems 'with a rather wide variety of non price-related decision rules. These are loosely enforced standards, rules of thumb, side bargains, cajoling, negotiations, special contingency plans, and in some cases literally shouting and screaming.'[42] In some respects, of course, the two 'firms' may not be competitors, but rather content each to have a major and clearly defined role in running aspects of the business. Conflict may, therefore, remain latent if each has a share of the 'spoils'. The 'negotiated order' may tend to prove difficult to achieve only if some actors are obliged to stand by their wider commitment to the 'public interest', or where some are inclined to uphold their own personal preferences at any cost.

Trustees and Administrators

For a not-for-profit health agency in the public sector, the pursuit of the 'public interest' is considered to be of paramount concern. However, such an expression as the 'public interest' may be difficult to quantify, to the extent that both the administrator-firm and the doctor-firm may feel able to define the expression in terms which accord more with their own wishes. But where does this place the publicly appointed trustees/members in the decision-making process? It appears that few attempts have been made to define the objectives of public trustees, still less to assess what impact they might have upon the overall direction of the organisation.

Clarkson's analysis [43] is largely based on the likelihood that the non-profit environment gives the administrator greater scope to deviate from the rule of wealth maximisation than does the profit-making environment. One way of deviating is to acquire greater current (non-pecuniary) benefits for himself (the administrator), and for other employees. The question then becomes one of whether the trustees acquiesce or 'condone' such behaviour, or attempt to check it in particular ways. If the latter, then different forms of duopoly might exist, in which negotiation, bargaining and compromise become the mechanisms for agreement between trustees and administrators, and between trustees and doctors. Again, the possibility cannot be discounted that the utility functions of the various groups might be congruent, permitting alliances to be formed.

Summary

As has been seen, the issue of what influences behaviour is far from resolved in the health sector, for there exists a multiplicity of individuals and groups, all of whom wish, for a variety of reasons, to have a say in the determination and allocation of health resources. In consequence, while influential groups can be identified, the extent to which decision-making power resides exclusively in the hands of one specified group of individuals is unclear.

There is here a real difficulty in measuring influences on decision-making and power, especially in complex health organisations that incorporate large numbers of separate decision-makers. Hence, it becomes less than easy to identify the moment and place at which crucial decisions are taken, let alone who takes them, and still less where they originated.[44] Moreover, when it is difficult to be certain when and where crucial decisions are taken, it makes it even more difficult to decide who has the most powerful voice: the centre or the periphery; politicians or administrators; trustees or doctors. The deference that it is customary to pay to politicians in office is in a very real sense a deference to the democratic process itself. In consequence, administrators can never allow themselves to forget their involvement in, and commitment to, the policies and political preferences of the central or local government of the day. But it is quite another thing to create a model with administrators being involved merely with the carrying out of decisions, and policy-making left to politics, politicians and government. Rather:

the exact balance between ministerial and civil service power will very much depend on what is to be decided, the political circumstances surrounding it, and the relative abilities of civil servants and ministers. This last point is crucial. The balance of ability can often, in the end, determine the balance of power.[45]

As for the interplay between centre and periphery, the absence of a clear 'social welfare function' to be maximised creates real obstacles to concerted action. Confusion is created partly by the particular characteristics of 'health and well-being' as a commodity, and partly by problems associated with 'social welfare' as a set of activities. Factors such as personal motivations and professional ties will affect the extent of the periphery's conscious acceptance of central guidance; while the technical difficulties of interpreting the centre's signals and the extent of its experience and training in grappling with such difficulties will affect the periphery's ability to follow the spirit of government guidance.[46] In summary, the absence of a unitary value of the 'public interest' will help to ensure that people locally will be as much 'decision-makers' as their political 'masters', albeit at a different level of administration (see Chapter 6).

5 CONCLUSION

In essence, this chapter has surveyed and analysed individual and collective decision-making in the health sector by making use of the market analogy. In particular, much reference has been made to utility theory, and to those theories of the firm rooted in either maximising or satisficing behaviour. It has been seen that decisions emanating from health agencies can be viewed as the outcome of the forces of demand and supply as they impinge on the political stage.

There are many actors who appear on stage, or influence the play's production, to the extent that the idea of a well defined public purpose may be an illusion. Many actors would like to be more powerful than they are, so that they can clear a space around themselves in which they can move freely and without dependence on others. As a consequence, the boundaries of influence may conflict.

It might therefore be expected that, without checks, the exercise of discretion will lead to wide variations in the use of health resources. Each decision-maker, to a greater or lesser extent controlling the 'space' in which he operates, will aim to pursue his own objectives. This leads to the conclusion that, because people will seek to maximise their own utilities, close attention to motivations and incentives is necessary, so that the degree of discretion afforded is controlled appropriately.

Whether or not discretion constitutes a problem depends less on its existence and more on the manner in which it is exercised. Hence, it is important to see how the theories match up to revealed behaviour patterns. Indeed, if the point of the models is to predict or account for behaviour, then the crucial question is how the models relate to reality. In other words, the next step for research is to establish the relationship between the behaviour patterns attributed hypothetically to health agencies and their agents, and behaviour as it is verified empirically. Caution is necessary; intentions are one thing, outcomes another. In theory, it can be argued that the intention of all the actors is to maximise their utility functions; in practice, it is at least possible that the conflict which would result leads the same actors periodically to seek outcomes that satisfice their utility functions. Inevitably, such a conclusion must await the results of further empirical studies in this important but under-researched area.

NOTES

1. OECD, 'Social Change in OECD Countries 1950-1980', OECD Observer, no. 107 (1980).
2. K. Judge, 'Rationing Social Services: a Study of Resource Allocation and the Personal Social Services' (Heinemann, London, 1978).
3. P. J. Devine et al., 'An Introduction to Industrial Economics' (Allen and Unwin, London, 1977).
4. C. M. Lindsay et al., 'National Health Issues: the British Experience' (Roche Laboratories, Welwyn Garden, March 1980).
5. W. J. Baumol, The Firm and its Objectives, 'Economic Theory and Operations Analysis' (Prentice-Hall, Englewood Cliffs, New Jersey, 1972), Chapter 15.
6. R. Marris, 'Economic Theory of Managerial Capitalism' (Macmillan, London, 1964).
7. O. E. Williamson, 'The Economics of Discretionary Behaviour' (Prentice-Hall, Englewood Cliffs, New Jersey, 1963).
8. M. C. Sawyer, 'Theories of the Firm' (Weidenfeld and Nicolson, London, 1979).
9. H. A. Simon, 'Administrative Behaviour' (Macmillan, London, 1957).
10. R. M. Cyert and J. G. March, 'A Behavioural Theory of the Firm' (Prentice-Hall, Englewood Cliffs, New Jersey, 1963).
11. D. A. Hay and D. J. Morris, 'Industrial Economics: Theory and Practice' (Oxford University Press, Oxford, 1979).
12. C. V. Brown and P. M. Jackson, 'Public Sector Economics' (Martin Robertson, Oxford, 1978), p. 82.
13. A. Downs, 'An Economic Theory of Democracy' (Harper and Row, New York, 1957).
14. Lindsay, 'National Health Issues'.
15. A. Breton, Economics of Representative Democracy in IEA, 'The Economics of Politics' (IEA, London, 1979), p. 68.
16. A. Peacock, The Economics of Bureaucracy: an Inside View in IEA, 'The Economics of Politics', p. 122.
17. Lord Boyle of Handsworth, Ministers and the Administrative Process, 'Public Administration', vol. 58 (Spring 1980), p. 6.
18. G. Tullock, Bureaucracy and the Growth of Government, 'IEA Readings 21' (IEA, London, 1979), p. 24.
19. J. M. Buchanan, From Private Preferences to Public Philosophy, 'IEA Readings 18' (IEA, London, 1978), p. 11.
20. A. B. Atkinson and J. E. Stiglitz, Theories of the State and Public Economics, 'Lectures on Public Economics' (McGraw-Hill, New York, 1980), Lecture 10.
21. W. A. Niskanen, Competition among Government Bureaus, 'IEA Readings 18' (IEA, London, 1978), pp. 161-70.

22. Downs, 'An Economic Theory of Democracy'.
23. W. A. Niskanen, 'Bureaucracy and Representative Government' (Aldine Press, Chicago, 1971).
24. D. J. Storey, The Economics of Bureaux: the Case of London Boroughs 1970-76, 'Applied Economics' (June 1980), pp. 223-34.
25. Ibid.
26. Atkinson and Stiglitz, Theories of the State, p. 314.
27. T. Sudama, PPBS and Theories of Decision-Making, Bureaucracy, and Politics, 'Public Finance', vol. XXXII, no. 3 (1977), pp. 354-73.
28. Brown and Jackson, 'Public Sector Economics', p. 144.
29. M. L. Lee, A Conspicuous Production Theory of Hospital Behaviour, 'Southern Economic Journal', vol. 38, no. 1 (July 1971), pp. 48-58.
30. J. P. Newhouse, Toward a Theory of Nonprofit Institutions: an Economic Model of a Hospital, 'The American Economic Review' (March 1970), pp. 64-74.
31. P. J. Feldstein, 'Health Care Economics' (John Wiley and Sons, New York, 1979), Chapter 10.
32. P. Jacobs, A Survey of Economic Models of Hospitals, 'Inquiry' (June 1974), pp. 83-97.
33. Atkinson and Stiglitz, Theories of the State, p. 316.
34. J. L. Migue and G. Belanger, Towards a Theory of Managerial Discretion, 'Public Choice' (Spring 1974), pp. 27-47.
35. S. Harrison, The Politics of Health Manpower in A. Long and G. Mercer (eds.), 'Manpower Planning in the NHS' (Gower Press, Farnborough, 1981), p. 83.
36. M. Pauly and M. Redisch, The Not-for-Profit Hospital as a Physicians' Co-operative, 'The American Economic Review' (March 1973), pp. 87-99.
37. D. Mechanic, The Growth of Medical Technology and Bureaucracy: Implications for Medical Care, 'Milbank Memorial Fund Quarterly' (Winter 1977), pp. 61-78.
38. Jacobs, A Survey of Economic Models of Hospitals.
39. K. Lee, Health Care: Planning, Policies and Incentives, 'Futures' (December 1979), pp. 482-90.
40. Buchanan, From Private Preferences to Public Philosophy, pp. 4-5.
41. J. E. Harris, The Internal Organisation of Hospitals: Some Economic Implications, 'The Bell Journal of Economics', vol. 8, no. 2 (Autumn 1977), pp. 467-82.
42. Ibid., p. 478.
43. K. Clarkson, Some Implications of Property Rights in Hospital Management, 'Journal of Law and Economics' (October 1972), pp. 363-76.
44. K. Barnard, K. Lee and J. Reynolds, 'Tracing Decisions in the NHS', King's Fund Publication RC16 (December 1980).
45. P. Kellner and Lord Crowther-Hunt, 'The Civil Servants:

an Inquiry into Britain's Ruling Class' (Macdonald, London, 1980), p. 238.

46. See W. J. M. Mackenzie, 'Power and Responsibility in Health Care' (Oxford University Press, Oxford, 1979).

5 PLANS, PROGRAMMES AND BUDGETS

1 HISTORICAL PERSPECTIVE

Comprehensive and corporate approaches to planning are commonly considered to involve a sequence of activities, from defining objectives, through considering alternatives, to detailed programming and budgeting. Through this sequence, it is intended that plans will be reflected in budget allocations, and ultimately in operational activities. Two features of this sequence are the particular concern of this chapter:

(1) the framework for planning, within which issues of objectives, priorities and choices can be considered, including the categorisation of health activities; and
(2) the nature of the link between the two different, but interrelated, processes of planning and budgeting.

The first concern reflects an interest in how the debate about health sector development is structured: are options considered and choices made in terms of 'health care groups', or in terms of institutions (for instance, hospitals and health centres), or by diseases (infectious, chronic), or by type of activity (control, prevention, treatment, rehabilitation)? The way debates and discussions are structured will affect the range of options considered and, ultimately, the decisions made.

The second concern relates to the 'assumed tendency of bureaucracies to acquire a momentum of their own, and progressively to lose their orientation towards the objects they were instituted to pursue'.[1] Developments in economics and operations research have promised to assist in the determination of the optimum allocation of public funds between competing uses. Yet, even when the techniques of these disciplines are used in planning, there is frequently so great a gap between planning and budgeting that the content of the annual budget bears little relationship to the content of plans.[2]

While these two concerns are rather different in nature, they are handled together here for the simple reason that a particular framework has been developed, under the heading of a Planning, Programming, Budgeting System (PPBS), which encompasses both these issues. This framework aims to provide an appropriate structuring of the planning debate, and to introduce an explicit link between planning and budgeting.

Indeed, these can be said to be its two most important features.

PPBS has been described as 'the most sophisticated of the procedures of comprehensive decision-making'.[3] In brief, it represents an attempt to integrate three basic functions into a comprehensive system :

(1)   planning: that is a survey of the environment, the projection of future trends, the determination of goals and objectives;

(2)   programming: the formulation of programmes and projects;

(3)   budgeting: costing projects, their incorporation in annual budgets, the control of expenditure.

Implicit in the system is the subordination of budgeting to planning.[4]

PPBS also represents a reaction against those traditional forms of budgeting which categorise proposed expenditure mainly by the type of resource on which it is to be spent (such as staff, laundry or pharmacy), rather than by the purpose of the expenditure. In other words, traditional budgets have focused on 'inputs' and historically have been developed in the interests of financial control and audit. One of the main aims of a PPBS, however, is to analyse the use of resources by the various purposes they serve (i.e. by programmes) and relate resources used to results achieved, or 'outputs'.

Some confusion is caused by the variety of ways in which terms such as programme budgets and PPBS are used. Some writers use these terms synonymously, others see them as forms of 'output budgeting'. In this chapter, a clear distinction is made between a programme budget and a PPB System. The former is considered to be that part of the PPBS which is based upon the budget, and sets out over a number of years historical trends and future plans, organised into programmes. As such, it is an integral part of a PPBS, but is no more than a particular way of organising information on inputs, activities and outputs. A full PPB System would, in addition, aim to establish arrangements to link systematically the planning of policies and priorities with resource allocations and with the financial planning system, to relate individual decisions to an overall framework, and to assess the effectiveness with which all resources are deployed.

PPBS as such is still a relatively recent innovation. Though historical antecedents can be traced, it is commonly regarded as having been developed by the US Defence Department under McNamara. Subsequently, the then President of the US, Lyndon Johnson, decreed that the approach should be adopted by all federal agencies, in what has been termed an attempt to 'recast federal budgeting from a repetitive process for financing permanent bureaucracies into an instrument for deciding the purposes and programmes of government'.[5] The experiment was not considered a success, disillusionment set in and, in 1971, agencies were permitted to cease using PPBS. However, while the US moved on to other approaches, many countries are still experimenting with PPBS or with modified versions such as programme budgeting. Indeed, a somewhat cynical commentator has written: 'Although there is no evidence that programme budgeting works in the US ... it has nonetheless been exported throughout the world.'[6]

Thus, for example, the UK government considered the possibility of introducing PPBS in 1970 (though finally decided to establish a much more selective approach to policy analysis); the UK Department of Health and Social Security (DHSS) began as early as 1971 to set up its own programme budget; and WHO guidance on national health planning incorporates recommendations on the adoption of programme budgeting. However, as many have noted, the now commonly used term programme budgeting lacks the precise meaning of PPBS and, more realistically perhaps, is concerned primarily with methods of relating expenditure to main purposes or activities.

None the less, the fundamental problems that PPBS was devised to tackle still remain, and PPBS lives on in an attenuated form. Moreover, the experience of attempts to introduce programme budgeting into a number of countries provides very useful insights into how organisations react to attempts to alter their traditional ways of behaviour, and into what means might be most appropriate to encourage a more considered and analytical approach to planning and budgeting inside government agencies in the health sector.

2 CONCEPTS OF PROGRAMME BUDGETING

Like any planning system, PPBS encompasses a particular set of values. It was developed largely by economists, and reflected their concern that in governmental, non-profit-making organisations where market or profit tests were absent, efforts should be made to relate inputs to outputs in order to achieve maximum efficiency. Thus planning in the context of PPBS is seen as a means of optimising in the economist's sense, that is of equating marginal product and cost in different activities. In consequence, one of the main aims of a PPBS is to analyse the allocation of resources in terms of the purposes to be served, and to relate the resources used to the results achieved.

These tasks are to be carried out by establishing:

(1) the aims and objectives of the organisation;
(2) the activities which contribute to these objectives;
(3) the resources or inputs which are being devoted to
     different objectives; and
(4) the outputs which result from the use of those
     resources.

These elements are brought together in a programme budget.
A programme is made up of all activities, inputs and outputs,
contributing to a common aim or objective, or a group of
common aims. Each programme may have sub-programmes, and
can cover a number of years, both past and future.

A full PPBS incorporates what its title would suggest,
namely Planning, or the development of goals, objectives and
priorities; Programming, the formulation and analysis of
alternative ways of reaching objectives; Budgeting, translating
the most desirable alternative into resource requirements; and
System, reflecting a concern for a total, continuing process,
involving the interaction of all parts and activities of the
organisation, assisted by a continuous evaluation of the impact
of programmes.

In short, a full system would probably incorporate the
following features:

(1) regular reviews of plans expressed in the form of a
     programme budget;
(2) a formal link with the normal budgeting processes;
     and
(3) special studies of particular areas where programme
     budget information suggested that the utilisation of
     resources might be improved, or where deeper review
     seemed desirable. Cost-benefit and cost-effectiveness
     analysis are particularly associated with a PPBS.

It has already been implied that severe methodological
difficulties arise in introducing a PPBS. Five key issues can
be isolated.

(1) The definition of objectives and programme struc-
     tures. An organisation's objectives may prove difficult
     to define systematically. Moreover it can be argued
     that the set of programmes appropriate to an organ-
     isation at any one time will depend on the main
     choices it faces, for PPBS is intended to direct atten-
     tion to the importance of trade-offs both within and
     between programmes. For instance, if programmes are
     defined too narrowly, analyses within programmes may
     be made easier, but at the expense of losing sight of
     interdependencies between programmes.
(2) The allocation of activities and resources between

programmes. In this respect, classification problems arise where activities serve more than one purpose, and hence could be classified under more than one programme. Where activities contribute to different programmes, apportionment of costs is often difficult.

(3) The definition and measurement of costs. The nature and type of cost information demanded by PPBS is likely to be very different from that contained within conventional cost accounts. Thus methods for obtaining these costs need to be developed, for it will rarely be possible to change the basic accounting system. Moreover, attention should be paid not only to private costs (those costs imposed on the organisation by its activities) but also to the costs those activities impose on outside individuals or groups (social costs).

(4) The definition and measurement of outputs. The approach of devising programmes on the basis of objectives and outputs presupposes that objectives can be articulated and outputs measured. Yet final output measures that reflect the degree of attainment of objectives may be elusive.

(5) The analysis and evaluation of selected activities and expenditures. Some commentators have seen this as the most significant part of PPBS. It essentially involves the application of cost-benefit analysis, cost-effectiveness analysis and systems analysis.[7]

It can be argued, moreover, that PPBS is particularly susceptible to methodological problems when applied in the health sector, where objectives may be quite unclear, and outputs difficult to measure and quantify. The next section, therefore, looks at the application of programme budgeting to the health sector in the UK, and at the approach of WHO to programme budgeting, before returning to a detailed consideration of the five important issues raised above.

3 THE APPLICATION OF PROGRAMME BUDGETING TO HEALTH SERVICES

In the 1960s and 1970s, several UK government departments experimented with PPBS, notably the Department of Education and Science and the Department of Health and Social Security. The DHSS approach, in particular, represents an interesting contrast to that of the US. The term 'output budget' was rejected by the DHSS in favour of 'programme budget', on the grounds that its major concern was to link policy formulation with the availability of resources, and that health policies were usually expressed in terms of services rather than outputs.[8] Thus the PB was not primarily conceived as being the means of relating costs to output and of evaluating outputs. Indeed, other government procedures (programme analysis and review, or PAR) had been introduced to undertake this task on a selective basis.

Moreover, the DHSS explicitly rejected the use of a programme budget for operational management. Instead, programme budgeting was to be used primarily for planning, and in particular:

(1)   to assist in the DHSS internal planning system;
(2)   to act as a basis for guidelines to the NHS; and
(3)   to act as a means for monitoring and control.

In terms of assisting in its own planning, the DHSS felt that the programme budget would:

(1)   show more clearly how resources were used, and what outputs and benefits they produced, to help with the consideration of future priorities;
(2)   suggest areas where cost effectiveness comparisons would be useful, by bringing together different activities serving similar needs;
(3)   improve the forecasting of expenditure under existing policies, by showing how trends in different factors contributed to the total demand for resources;
(4)   show the reasons for rising demands and uses for extra resources and, therefore, help the DHSS get adequate resources.[9]

These hoped-for benefits have to be seen in the context of the role of the DHSS in relation to the NHS. Historically, the DHSS had confined itself largely to allocating resources geographically, and issuing guidance on service developments. Hence, it was first attracted to programme budgeting as a means of costing policies, to consider priorities within realistic financial constraints, and to explore future strategies. The programme budget thus became the technical basis of strategic guidance issued to the NHS, namely of the documents 'Priorities for the Health and Personal Social Services'[10] and 'The Way Forward'.[11] While these documents did provide growth rates and programme shares (in financial terms) for each programme, it was stressed in 'The Way Forward' that 'the details . . . simply provide illustrative indications of the national long-term direction of strategic development within resource constraints; they do not represent specific targets to be achieved by declared dates in any localities.'

During the late 1970s, however, it became increasingly clear to the DHSS that, if it wished to discover the extent to which local plans were compatible with national priorities, and the extent to which national policies needed to be adjusted in the light of local changes, then this could best be achieved if local plans adopted the form and structure of the programme budget developed centrally. Accordingly, in 1978, health authorities were requested to adopt a new system for transmitting planning intentions to the DHSS which, in effect, demanded the production of a local programme budget.[12] In any case, the DHSS argued, this information was necessary for realistic strategic planning to take place at the local level.

The programme budget structure adopted by the DHSS was relatively simple and was influenced considerably by the need to produce a programme classification that would embrace both health and personal social services. No attempt was made to specify objectives in the 'Priorities' document or subsequently; instead, broad programmes were chosen, representing a combination of client and target groups, which the 'Priorities' document stated would be:

> more meaningful in considering options and priorities than the public expenditure survey breakdown, or the traditional estimates and accounts . . . there are certain major groups of services cutting across administrative boundaries, which provide complementary and alternative forms of care for certain important groups of users, in particular, the elderly, physically and mentally handicapped, mentally ill, and children.

The basic programme structure consisted of general and acute hospital services; primary care services; elderly; mental illness; mentally handicapped; children; maternity; and younger physically handicapped. It can be noted that this programme structure represented essentially a compromise between the desire to analyse alternative or complementary ways of providing services in response to health and social problems, and the need to take account of the availability of suitable information.

The DHSS has not, as yet, placed much emphasis on specifying or measuring outputs, relying instead on measures of intermediate output such as patient days, or even of inputs, such as expenditure per head. Programme budgeting in England has thus come to mean primarily the attaching of costing information to broad programmes of activities, and its use for establishing options and priorities, and considering the pace of implementation of national policies. This might help to explain why, despite DHSS encouragement, local health authorities in England have been reluctant to embark on programme budgeting. (In contrast, a programme budget on broadly similar lines to that of the DHSS has been developed for the local level in Scotland[13], and is being used to investigate the efficiency and cost-effectiveness of services.[14]) None the less, while few local health authorities were in practice operating a programme budget, they were encouraged by the organisational structure of the NHS, and by the procedures of the planning system, to structure the planning debate in programme terms. Officers were appointed with special responsibilities for particular health care groups (such as children and the elderly), planning teams were set up for similar health care groups, and authorities were increasingly required to submit costed plans and projects according to the programme structure of the DHSS. The aim of these arrangements is clear: by so structuring the planning system, institutionally based planning was to be discouraged, and planning for health care groups encouraged.

Another approach to programme budgeting is that provided by the World Health Organization. It has defined programme budgeting as 'making sure that budgets are available to attain programme objectives'.[15] The Organization argues that programme budgeting provides for better decision-making and implementation, both by defining objectives clearly and by grouping together the resources required to attain each objective. A programme is intended to consist of a series of interrelated actions aimed at reaching defined objectives, such as the improvement of child health or the provision of safe drinking water.[16] The actions in each programme are to be spelt out in terms of: objectives with related targets; manpower, technology, physical facilities, equipment and supplies required; means of evaluation; financial estimates; a calendar for action; and ways of ensuring appropriate co-ordination.

This approach, therefore, essentially sees programme budgeting as a way of ensuring that plans are reflected in actual budgets, that quantitative targets are set, and that all the logistical aspects of planning are tackled. WHO states explicitly that programme budgeting is a means of ensuring that programme decisions become budget decisions. Thus, in contrast to much of the US and UK experience, programme budgeting is not seen primarily as a way of assisting the development of priorities or programmes. Rather, the formulation of policies and the definition of priorities take place prior to the construction of a programme budget. This example thereby emphasises that the attractions of programme budgeting are likely to vary from one setting to another, depending on the motivations of its proponents.

4 KEY ISSUES OF METHODOLOGY

And yet, whatever particular form of programme budgeting is implemented, a number of methodological issues will have to be faced. These were identified earlier as being:

(1) the definition of objectives and programme structures;
(2) the allocation of activities and resources between programmes;

(3) the definition and measurement of costs;
(4) the definition and measurement of outputs;
(5) the analysis and evaluation of particular activities.

Each of these issues is considered in turn below, with the assistance of illustrative material from the UK.

The Definition of Objectives and Programmes

In its comprehensive form, PPBS aims to set up a hierarchy of objectives, with broad, overall objectives being subdivided into more specific goals, to permit an analysis of the extent to which different activities contribute to the goals of the organisation. To offer an example, the contribution to the goal of national defence of expenditure by the Defence Department on health would, in the first instance, be weighed against the contribution to defence of other input activities for which health expenditure is a substitute. In principle, the aim of the analysis would be to seek to use the quantity of health input that would, under diminishing returns, bring its marginal contribution to exact equality with the marginal contribution of other inputs.[17] In welfare economics terms, this procedure would lead to the optimum allocation of resources.

In the health field, however, as in other fields of social policy, it is evident that there is a multiplicity of objectives, many not held in common, and many in direct conflict with each other. A variety of alternative programme structures can be envisaged, based on different concepts of the function and goals of health services. Thus programmes could be structured according to:

(1) target groups - defined by criteria of age, sex, income level, social group, geographical area - irrespective of health need;
(2) client groups, such as the mentally handicapped, with health problems in common;
(3) type of function of services - prevention, treatment, support, rehabilitation;
(4) broad disease problems;
(5) diagnostic groups;
(6) clinical specialties; or
(7) degree of dependence - the extent to which patients are judged to be in need of medical, nursing or social care.

A decision on which structure(s) is most appropriate must rest ultimately on the scope and nature of the strategic choices the organisation believes it is likely to face in the future. Yet there are other constraints on the structure of programmes. The more numerous the programmes, the more each will be homogeneous, and the easier it will be to look at strategies and trade-offs within each programme. On the other hand, a multiplicity of programmes carries the disadvantage that interdependencies across programmes will be more difficult to establish. Yet broad programmes may also be unhelpful. The 'acute medical services' programme in the UK incorporates many diverse specialties, and has not turned out to be a useful programme for strategic analysis. Moreover, it has proved extremely difficult, if not impossible, for programme budgeting to facilitate trade-offs between radically different programmes such as health and defence.

A further point is that the desire to set up programmes that are attractive from a conceptual point of view must be tempered by the availability of suitable information. The further programme structures move away from organisational boundaries, the more difficult it becomes to obtain information relevant to those structures. In short, the complexities are so real that they have led some commentators to reject the detailed analysis of programmes and objectives: 'The fixation on programme structure with objectives and information is the most pernicious aspect of PB.'[18]

Allocation of Activities

In an 'ideal' PPBS, the boundaries of the health sector would be drawn as widely as possible, and incorporate all health-related expenditure. Yet this would create an enormous demand for information from public, private and voluntary agencies and produce severe problems of access to, and collation of, data. Moreover, as any particular health activity is likely to serve a number of different purposes, the issue arises of how to allocate overall expenditure to the various programmes. This problem, one of splitting 'joint costs', arises even within a relatively simple programme structure such as that adopted in the UK. Here, for the sake of simplicity if not accuracy, the decision was taken to allocate services to programmes in terms of their 'major user'. The justification was that, at an aggregate level, the figures were approximately correct; yet at a local level such crude calculations are likely to be misleading.

Definition and Measurement of Costs

It is generally agreed that traditional budgets and cost accounts rarely provide information in a form which will prove suitable for programme budgeting. This problem is compounded in the health sector where hospital production functions are unclear[19], and where no charges may be made for treatment and hence no costing (or billing) of individual treatments done. For instance, in the UK, little attention has traditionally been paid to discovering the treatment costs of patients, emphasis being placed rather on controlling total expenditure.

Indeed, the costing problems associated with programme budgeting in the UK provide a good illustration of those faced by many countries.

The original concept of PPBS was as a tool to optimise the allocation of resources within society as a whole, and not merely within the public sector. The appropriate cost measure includes, therefore, costs imposed on the community at large, not merely those costs that fall on government. Yet PPBS has tended to focus exclusively on health service agencies. For instance, the programme budget of the DHSS implicitly defined its scope as the public agencies providing health and personal social services. Other DHSS documents have taken an even narrower definition, to the extent of excluding family practitioner services, on the basis that they are not financed out of the allocations to health authorities, and should not, therefore, feature in any priority-setting process. Needless to say, such attempts to restrict the 'health sector' to those services for which there is a statutory responsibility and/or for which data are available may well distort overall priorities by giving insufficient weight to the costs borne by related services or by private individuals.

While data on treatment costs necessary for a programme budget are not routinely produced by the NHS accounting system, there has been increased interest within the UK in specialty costing.[20] Previously, such data were generated only through research studies [21] or by the analysis of aggregate data at national level. However, figures produced by such methods did not necessarily bear any close relationship to the costs faced by individual health authorities. As the DHSS itself recognised:

> For longer term planning, what is needed is a means of estimating costs which is quick and simple, so that many alternatives can be explored; which is related to levels of service provision or 'output' rather than resources used, since this is what strategic planning is concerned with; but which is nevertheless accurate enough to avoid unrealistic planning.[22]

The DHSS considered four possible methods for estimating specialty costs:

(1) tertiary analysis in a routine costing system;
(2) detailed studies to allocate shared costs in the particular hospitals of interest;
(3) multiple regression analysis;
(4) adopting working assumptions, for instance that costs in single specialty hospitals were similar to those in the same specialties in general hospitals.[23]

The first option, for detailed specialty costing to be done

routinely at the local level, was not thought either appropriate or feasible. Rather, for strategic planning purposes, health authorities were encouraged to use average costs by broad specialty estimated from aggregate data.

In general, the appropriateness of any one of these costing methods can be said to depend on the purpose for which costing information is sought. In respect of the testing of options within the context of strategic planning, what is appropriate is, in effect, a method to assess the long-term impact of the changes proposed on total expenditure. In other words, marginal costs are needed for planning purposes, yet undue reliance is often placed upon average (unit) costs. Why is this emphasis on average costs misconceived?

Average costs per case are likely to vary from hospital to hospital, depending on the influence of such factors as the age and location of physical facilities, occupancy rates; length of stay, case mix, complexity of case mix and quality of care given. In addition, hospitals are multi-product firms, differing in the quantities they produce of education, research, community care, out-patient services and, their predominant activity, in-patient care. Thus average cost changes, calculated at an aggregate level and reflecting variations in the volume and composition of hospital activity, are unlikely to prove sensitive enough to explore the impact of local strategies on future expenditure. When such strategies imply changes in the work-load of particular hospitals, marginal costs are more relevant than average costs, and account must be taken of the size and importance of these numerous variables in considering the cost behaviour of individual hospitals. In consequence, it may be necessary for health authorities to maintain two types of costing: the first to show in broad terms what expenditure goes on which care group; and the second to indicate the relevant costs of particular policy decision.

In the context of planning, therefore, when any attempt is made to push programme budgeting to the lower management levels of the health service, obtaining costing information appropriate to that level is likely to be a major problem. The major issue is likely to be less one of technical feasibility than of the availability of skilled analysts who have sufficient time to devote to costing, and to the development of a simple, but sufficiently accurate, methodology that bears on marginal costs, not average costs.

Definition and Measurement of Outputs

The definition and measurement of outputs in the health sector represent a thorny problem, if measures of 'final' output, such as changes in health status, are sought. Since output can be defined as 'effectiveness in attaining an objective', the most appropriate output measure is determined by the way in which programmes are defined. The lower the level at which objectives are articulated, the easier it will be to find an output measure, but the greater the number of incommensurable measures there will be to knit together at higher levels.

Moreover, many activities have multiple objectives, and therefore multi-dimensional outputs. The use of devices such as health status indices to reduce these to a common unit of measurement, though not yet generally applicable, may eventually prove useful.[24] Yet even if accurate output measurement is not at present possible, the identification of the type of output, and the classification of costs accordingly, may still reveal important relevant strategic features of the situation.

In the absence of easily accessible output measures, indicators of 'intermediate' output tend to be used, and many programme budgets rely on measures such as cost per case. Yet this measure gives no indication of whether, for instance, higher unit costs in one area than another are justified because a higher-quality service is provided. Moreover, there is no way of knowing what part of the unit cost arises from factors beyond the health agency's control, such as capital stock that is expensive to run or local labour market difficulties.

While it is difficult to suggest an alternative approach, the danger is that attention is focused exclusively on inputs. Thus some programme budgets have been formulated largely as a means of allocating expenditure to various programmes and testing the feasibility of strategies, rather than as an output-orientated framework for planning and priority setting. Valuing outputs may be very difficult, but some progress might be made in identifying and measuring them, and developing indicators of effectiveness.

Analysis and Evaluation

The prime tools of analysis in a PPBS are cost-effectiveness and cost-benefit analyses, both representing ways of helping to determine how resources can best be allocated between competing social objectives. Cost-effectiveness analysis, one of the newer tools of public expenditure policy analysis, aims to identify either the programme capable of achieving certain specified goals at the lowest possible cost, or the programme which will maximise the benefit to be gained from a given defined budget. In either case, one of the parameters is fixed and the objective is to maximise the benefit or to minimise the cost.[25]

Cost-benefit analysis is the organised consideration of the disadvantages and advantages of alternative policy options in terms of a common denominator, namely a common value unit or numeraire (often a unit of money) and a common point of incidence, both in terms of time and in terms of a target, such as a nation, a region or the economy. Cost-benefit analysis attempts to value all socially relevant outcomes and state whether a policy is worth implementing, unlike cost-effectiveness analysis which takes an objective as given.

An extensive literature exists on these techniques[26], though it is useful to identify here some of the key problems of application, and how they have been tackled. The problem of specifying outputs appears most acutely in cost-benefit analysis, which demands that benefits not only be measured, but also valued. In particular, the issue of valuing life must be faced, and this highlights the unsatisfactory nature of many of the approaches that are at present available.[27] Allied to this issue is the major problem of establishing the link between inputs and outputs; that is, of ascertaining that particular expenditures have an impact on health status. Finally, in any particular analysis, only some of the variables can be quantified. Many costs and benefits will be imponderable, such as the likely pay-off from basic research, or the value of avoiding suffering and pain, though they will need to be given due consideration in any analysis.

How, then, given these conceptual and methodological problems, can such techniques help in planning and programme budgeting? Examples are available from the US Department of Health, Education and Welfare, where various studies have been carried out as an integral part of the PPBS. These have attempted to set up one or more objectives, and to compare alternative approaches to reaching these objectives in terms of their incremental cost effectiveness. For instance, an analysis of maternal, infant and child health care considered the extent to which different programmes would achieve the main objective of making maternal and child health services available and accessible to all; and sub-objectives were specified in terms of reducing infant mortality rates, reducing unmet dental needs, and reducing the incidence and prevalence of handicaps.[28] Another study looked at disease control programmes, in an attempt to answer the question: if additional money were to be allocated to various disease control programmes, which would show the highest pay-off in terms of lives saved and disability prevented per dollar spent?[29]

In the UK, by contrast, work on the programme budget has focused largely on measuring inputs. While some cost-benefit and cost-effectiveness studies have been commissioned, these have not formed a regular part of programme budgeting activity. At local level, virtually no experience of such studies exists, nor staff to undertake them. This picture might change before too long, given an increasing acceptance that:

the most fundamental limitation of the programme budget developed for health and personal social services is that it does not provide the information needed to evaluate alternative policies in depth. It provides a framework for deciding priorities in implementing policies, but there is no point in planning to implement policies which are themselves misconceived because they are not based on adequate thought, consultation and research.[30]

5 THE ORGANISATIONAL CONTEXT OF PROGRAMME BUDGETING

Discussion in this chapter has concentrated so far largely on the methodological or technical issues of programme budgeting. However, it would be unwise to assume that programme budgeting is merely a technical exercise; rather, close attention needs to be given to the organisational context within which any programme budgeting approach is to be applied. Indeed, as American experience has shown, the behaviour of vested interests within an organisation is crucial to the effectiveness of PPBS, and an examination of the reasons for its failure within the US provides useful lessons for other countries:

> PPB failed to penetrate because the budgeters didn't let it in and the PPB'ers didn't know how to break down the resistance. But even if the leadership, data, analytic capability, resources and support, interpersonal and institutional sensitivity, and all the factors which worked against PPB, had been favourable, there still would have been the anti-analytic thrust of the budget process to contend with.[31]

In short, PPBS was conceived as a device to help planners control the budget and make it more 'rational'. However, the economic values it reflected of attaining efficiency in the use of resources were not necessarily the values of others involved in the planning and budgetary processes. For instance, it has been argued that the incremental mode of budgeting enshrines important American values, in that it gives expression and representation to diverse political interests. To adherents of the pluralist approach, this procedure is sacrosanct, and should take priority over the maximisation of a consistent set of objectives. Thus, for instance, the process of 'health production' may be perceived as important in itself, in contrast to the focus of the economist on inputs and outputs. Moreover, PPBS does not necessarily absolve anyone from the obligations of the conventional budgetary system. Indeed the penalties for breaking the conventional rules of budgeting may be more severe than those for circumventing PPBS.

Other general lessons can be drawn from US experience, for instance, that programme budgeting requires that the leader(s) of the organisation be committed to it. Thus McNamara was responsible for introducing and maintaining

PPBS in the US Defence Department; and Health Ministers in Britain throughout the 1970s appeared to appreciate the assistance the programme budget gave them, both in deciding upon priorities and in strengthening their hand in any discussions they had with the Treasury for extra resources. In both these instances it can be argued that programme budgeting enabled key decision-makers to strengthen their position. While this may appear to question hypotheses advanced earlier, that a Minister will normally be more interested in maintaining his options open than committing himself to long-term plans, the opportunity for increasing control over the direction of the organisation may be a very tempting proposition.

And yet, at the same time, the success of PPBS will depend on those lower down the organisation who have to make it work. Unless their objectives are reconsidered, they will attempt to achieve the same ends within the new system as they did within the old, and the net result - in terms of the pattern of health services - may be little different. Hence, programme budgeting, by threatening established interests and questioning existing activities, is likely to stimulate such interests to defend their programmes and oppose programme budgeting, or manipulate it to their advantage.

A further illustration of the potency of these organisational considerations is provided by Caiden and Wildavsky in a large study of planning and budgeting processes in a number of poor countries.[32] They concluded that programme budgeting had most unwisely been exported to many developing countries, and represented a vain attempt to remedy what were seen as widespread defects in the budgeting and accounting procedures of governments. They observed that poverty and uncertainty permeated government budgeting in poor countries, and inevitably led to tactics which offered room for manoeuvre for the key actors. Such tactics included favouring short-term rather than long-term commitments, political bargaining not economic analysis, and flexibility over hard and fast allocations. Merely altering procedures or introducing a new technical framework for analysis left the basic conditions which led to these tactics unchanged. Thus the conclusion that matching programme budgeting to the conventional budgetary system is both a technical and a political issue is not confined only to the US. In some respects, the DHSS has avoided these problems by largely divorcing the programme budget from the budgeting process, and confining it to assisting the planning process. Even so, programme budgeting has been drawn increasingly into the political arena as the basis for central guidelines to local health authorities, and the framework for the feedback of plans and information to the centre.

A number of political commentators view the adoption of a PPB system as an attempt to increase central control, in that it represents a top-down approach to budgeting. Under a

PPBS, the top or political level makes decisions on broad goals, strategies, objectives, and these are transformed into programmes lower down the hierarchy; in a traditional budgeting system the lower levels determine the policy framework through the programmes they formulate autonomously, which are then aggregated at a higher level. Thus, Wildavsky has written: 'The PB could only be put together by the top executive. A more useful tool for increasing his power to control decisions vis-a-vis his subordinates would be hard to find.'[33]

Other commentators point out that, in practice, it is often the officials at the lower levels who originate programmes and that the system demands interaction, rather than domination, if it is to survive. The DHSS, for instance, makes frequent play of the point that it sees the NHS planning system as an interactive process. Yet, at the same time, it is apparent that the programme budgeting approach of the DHSS requires it to demand from local health authorities more and more explicit information, couched in terms that will enable it to be matched with the central programme budget. In this sense, therefore, the planning system is showing signs of increasing centralisation. Indeed, programme budgeting may be attractive to the DHSS partly as a means of increasing its knowledge and hence control of NHS activities.

Yet there are strong factors which militate against over-centralisation, as explored in Chapter 6. While the programme budget can act as the basis for policy guidance, the message contained in guidelines is often imprecise and unclear to local health agencies. The central level will usually be ignorant of local production functions, national guidance cannot allow for or adjust to all local circumstances, and the more precisely guidelines are worded, the more they will be vulnerable to changing events. Thus central guidance can at best point local health authorities in the right direction, rather than identify precise targets. What has to be lived with, in consequence, is that not even a programme budget enables national policies to be expressed in clear, quantitative terms at the local level.

Local disenchantment with, or indeed resistance to, programme budgeting is likely to emerge if the format of the programme budget, and the programme structuring promoted by the planning system, are centrally laid down and do not correspond with a local perceived need for analysis, quantitative information or systems for structuring issues. In the late 1970s, the DHSS encountered considerable resistance from local health agencies to its request for programme information and analysis. Insufficient acknowledgement of the technical problems (particularly of costing) was certainly one cause, especially in those health authorities which undertook much teaching and research, and thus had complex production functions. Yet technical problems provided only a partial explanation. The agencies' reluctance stemmed also from their unwillingness to pass what they regarded as speculative and inaccurate data to higher levels of management, for fear that such data would later be used for control purposes. Moreover, not all authorities were convinced that programme budgeting would help them, and preferred to operate on a more incrementalist basis. Even if they were convinced, they preferred to view programme budgeting as a mechanism for generating and testing options, rather than as a means of communication with higher levels.

A further lesson to be learnt, therefore, is that one programme structure does not necessarily suit the circumstances of all health authorities. But even if programme budgeting is adapted to local circumstances, an important issue is whether it is likely to be used for decision-making. A recurring theme of this book is that issues tend to be dealt with as they emerge, on an incremental basis, rather than slotted into a care group approach within a comprehensive overall strategy. At the local level in the UK, while much planning activity has been couched in care group terms, in practice various programme structures have existed simultaneously; the balance between care groups has been considered only in very general terms; capital-focused planning has persisted; and little appreciation has been apparent of the significance of structuring the planning debate in particular ways. Indeed, important local planning groups still exist which promote specifically medical, hospital-oriented views, thus reducing the influence of more broadly constituted health care planning teams. Moreover, the potential for using a programme budget to focus on analysis and evaluation has largely been ignored. Authorities have recently begun to use specialty costs to test the feasibility of projects and plans, but little attention has been paid to the notion of cost effectiveness, emphasis being placed either on costs (that is, what can be afforded within budget constraints) or effectiveness (in practice, what is medically desirable).

Indeed, given the extremely complex decision-making environment, and the influence wielded by members of the medical profession, managers have tended to be more concerned to negotiate a compromise between the various interest groups that surround them than to place their trust in quantitative analysis. While this conclusion may appear pessimistic, it again reinforces a point made earlier that plans (and programme budgets) cannot be divorced from the political climate within which they are expected to operate.

6 THE FUTURE OF PROGRAMME BUDGETING

What then is the potential for a form (or forms) of programme budgeting? Some of the analysts involved in the post-mortem following the demise of PPBS in the US have concluded that planning and policy analysis fitted uncomfortably with budgeting. Wildavsky, for instance, has recommended that this link should be broken, and other ways found of ensuring that policy analysis affects budgeting.[34] He also argues that policy analysis should not attempt to encompass all areas of expenditure, but rather should concentrate on those where the pay-off is likely to be greatest (cf. the mixed-scanning strategy).

The basic question remains, however, whether, and to what extent, programme budgeting will improve decision-making. As Schick has said, PPBS assumes that 'the form in which information is classified and used governs the actions of budget-makers, and conversely, that alterations in forms will produce desired changes in behaviour'.[35] None the less, Wildavsky counters:

> Those who could exert power need objectives to fight for. It is neither fashionable nor efficient to appear to seek power for its own sake. In polite society, the drive is masked and given a noble face when it can be attached to grand policy concerns that bring benefits to others as well as to power seekers.[36]

but Schick goes on to point out that:

> If information influences behaviour, the reverse is also true. Indeed, data are more tractable than roles; participants are more likely to seek out and use data which suit their preferences than to alter behaviour automatically in response to formal changes.

While economist planners, in promoting programme budgeting and policy analysis, may have the aim of injecting an element of what they perceive to be 'rationality' in the allocation of resources, other groups involved in policy-making may have different objectives, such as promoting consensus or ensuring the consistency of bureaucratic decisions. And making policies and analysis explicit may increase conflict within an organisation, and make it more difficult to reach decisions.

In the UK, the DHSS has to some extent avoided these problems encountered within the US by adopting a much simpler and more pragmatic version of programme budgeting. It also faces, however, an extremely complex environment both in the relationship between the DHSS and local levels of the health service, and within each of these local levels. It is evident that even a simplified programme budget, consisting largely of the analysis of expenditure by broad programmes and relying heavily on 'intermediate' outputs, has not been perceived as relevant or feasible by many health authorities, and has not stood up well to acting as the main means of communication between centre and periphery.

The question therefore arises of whether it is possible to identify the necessary and sufficient conditions under which a national programme budget can be seen to be equally relevant by local health agencies. Technical aspects, particularly of costing, are likely to be a major problem even where there is some local expertise, and considerable commitment will be required to resolve them. In relation to organisational behaviour, whether local health officers will be encouraged to develop an appreciation of programme structures depends crucially upon the incentives (and deterrents) in existence to induce or cajole such officers to structure their planning debate in these terms. In short: programme structures, whether for national governments or for local populations and agencies, must be devised to fit in with the system of incentives, political processes and administrative organisations within which planning will be carried out; alternatively, the incentive structure must be materially changed to effect the necessary will and compliance.

NOTES

1. J. D. Pole, Programmes, Priorities and Budgets, 'British Journal of Preventive and Social Medicine', vol. 28 (1974), pp. 191-5.
2. A. Waterston, An Operational Approach to Development Planning, 'International Journal of Health Services', vol. 1, no. 3 (1971), pp. 223-52.
3. A. Faludi, 'Planning Theory' (Pergamon Press, Oxford, 1973).
4. T. Sudama, PPBS and Theories of Decision-Making, Bureaucracy and Politics, 'Public Finance', vol. XXXII, no. 3 (1977).
5. A. Schick, The Road to PPB in F. J. Lyden and E. G. Miller (eds.), 'Planning, Programming, Budgeting' (Markham, Chicago, 1972).
6. N. Caiden and A. Wildavsky, 'Planning and Budgeting in Poor Countries' (John Wiley and Sons, New York, 1974).
7. R. N. Grosse, Problems of Resource Allocation in Health in R. H. Haveman and J. Margolis (eds.), 'Public Expenditure and Policy Analysis' (Markham Publishing Company, Chicago, 1970); A. M. Rivlin, The Planning Programming Budgeting System in Health, Education and Welfare: Some Lessons from Experience in Haveman and Margolis, 'Public Expenditure and Policy Analysis'.
8. G. T. Banks, Programme Budgeting in the DHSS in T.A. Booth (ed.), 'Planning for Welfare: Social Policy and the Expenditure Process' (Basil Blackwell and Martin Robertson, Oxford, 1979).
9. G. T. Banks et al., 'Planning, Programming, Budgeting System for the Health and Social Services' (DHSS, mimeo., 1971).
10. DHSS, 'Priorities for the Health and Personal Social

Services' (HMSO, London, 1976).

11. DHSS, 'The Way Forward' (HMSO, London, 1977).
12. DHSS, 'Draft Addendum to "The NHS Planning System": Future Form and Content of Strategic Plans', under cover of 'Dear Regional Administrator' letter of 11 January 1978.
13. G. H. Mooney et al., 'Choices for Health Care' (Macmillan, London, 1980).
14. G. H. Mooney, Planning for Balance of Care of the Elderly, 'Scottish Journal of Political Economy' (June 1978); A. M. Gray and R. Steele, Beyond the Programme Budget: Economics and Resource Planning in the NHS, 'Hospital and Health Services Review' (March 1980).
15. WHO, 'Guiding Principles for the Managerial Process for National Health Development in Support of Strategies for Health for All by the Year 2000' (WHO, Geneva, 1980).
16. WHO, 'Formulating Strategies for Health for All by the Year 2000' (WHO, Geneva, 1979).
17. D. Novick (ed.), 'Program Budgeting, Program Analysis and the Federal Budget' (Rand Corporation, 1965).
18. A. Wildavsky, Rescuing Policy Analysis from PPBS, 'Public Administration Review' (March/April 1969).
19. S. E. Berki, 'Hospital Economics' (Lexington Books and D. C. Heath, Lexington, Mass., 1972).
20. Royal Commission on the NHS, 'Management of Financial Resources in the NHS', Research Paper No. 2 (HMSO, London, 1978).
21. M. Feldstein, 'Economic Analysis for Health Service Efficiency' (North Holland Publishing Company, Amsterdam, 1967); J. H. Babson, 'Disease Costing' (Manchester University Press, Manchester, 1973).
22. DHSS, 'Draft Addendum', 11 January 1978.
23. DHSS, 'Revenue Costing in Strategic Planning: Further Guidance on Completion of SASP Tables', under cover of 'Dear Regional Administrator' letter of 29 March 1978.
24. A. J. Culyer, R. Lavers and A. Williams, Social Indicators: Health, 'Social Trends', no. 2 (1971), pp. 31-42.
25. K. Lee and A. Mills, The Role of Economists and Economics in Health Service Planning: a General Overview in K. Lee (ed.), 'Economics and Health Planning' (Croom Helm, London, 1979).
26. K. E. Warner and R. C. Hutton, Cost-Benefit and Cost-Effectiveness Analysis in Health Care, 'Medical Care', vol. XVIII, no. 11 (1980); M. F. Drummond, 'Principles of Economic Appraisal in Health Care' (Oxford University Press, Oxford, 1980).
27. G. H. Mooney, 'The Valuation of Human Life' (Macmillan, London, 1977).
28. A. L. Levin, Cost Effectiveness in Maternal and Child Health, 'New England Journal of Medicine', vol. 278, no. 19 (9 May 1968).

29. R. N. Grosse, Cost Benefit Analysis in Disease Control Programs in M. G. Kendall (ed.), 'Cost Benefit Analysis' (The English Universities Press, London, 1971), pp. 17-34.
30. Banks, Programme Budgeting in the DHSS, p. 169.
31. A. Schick, A Death in the Bureaucracy: the Demise of Federal PPB, 'Public Administration Review' (March/April 1973), pp. 146-55.
32. Caiden and Wildavsky, 'Planning and Budgeting in Poor Countries'.
33. A. Wildavsky, 'The Politics of the Budgeting Process' (Little Brown and Company, Boston, 1964).
34. Wildavsky, Rescuing Policy Analysis from PPBS, p. 196.
35. Schick, The Road to PPB.
36. Wildavsky, Rescuing Policy Analysis from PPBS, p. 198.

6 RELATIONSHIPS BETWEEN CENTRAL GOVERNMENT AND PERIPHERAL HEALTH AGENCIES: THE ROLE OF PLANNING SYSTEMS

1 INTRODUCTION

In general, Western capitalist economies rely largely on the 'market' to organise the production and consumption of goods and services. Accordingly, the requirements of consumers and producers are mediated via the 'invisible hand' of the market, subject only to government provision of an appropriate framework within which such transactions can take place. Many governments, however, prefer not to leave production and consumption solely to the influence of market forces in certain sectors of the economy. The health sector is a case in point, for many governments intervene, either by providing services directly through a national health service, or indirectly by organising or regulating health agencies, providers and funding bodies.

Government intervention raises the crucial issue of the form which control should take and the level at which it should be exerted. Should control be centralised, with the national government organising and running health services itself? Or should some form of decentralised, or even devolved, control be introduced? It has been argued that:

the decentralisation of authority to identifiable subordinate agencies with their own staff is appropriate when it is impossible for the central authority to translate broad policies into specific instructions and when their interpretation near the point of delivery has a considerable impact on the quality of service provided.[1]

On the other hand, fundamental arguments about the value of equality and equal citizenship support the case against decentralisation or devolution, for decentralisation can impede the attainment of national goals and permit local decision-makers to meet their own, local, objectives.[2]

Arguments for and against centralisation can be generalised in the following way.[3] Decentralisation facilitates:

(1)   matching of services to local needs;
(2)   greater community involvement;
(3)   taking advantage of local knowledge;
(4)   local linkages between sectors; and
(5)   generation of commitment to implement decisions.

On the other hand, centralisation may promote:

(1)   greater equity between geographical areas;
(2)   a greater detachment from local pressures; and
(3)   accountability when funds are provided by central government.

Attention has focused increasingly on the important role of policy implementors. As Chapter 4 argued, public policy is usually carried out, or mediated, by actors or agencies who are not themselves involved in formulating national policy. Moreover, policies that emerge from a process of conflict and compromise are inevitably vulnerable to implementation problems. This argument favours decentralisation, as a means of involving local staff in decision-making, and thereby achieving local commitment to action.

This debate on centre-periphery relationships has direct relevance to health planning. Planning systems are frequently seen by their architects as mechanisms for maintaining some element of central control, while permitting considerable local discretion. This is a common feature in countries as diverse as Britain, Tanzania, Ghana and Chile (though to some extent these countries are linked by a common influence stemming from American corporate planning philosophies). For example, the health planning system of the UK affirms that 'decentralisation of decision-making, implicit in the patient-centred approach, can be balanced with the need for national and Regional strategic direction by means of a planning system'; that 'there should be maximum decentralisation and delegation of decision-making, but within policies established at Regional and Area levels'; and that 'delegation downwards should be matched with accountability upwards.'[4] While this slogan of 'delegation downwards, accountability upwards' has been described as an 'utterly unintelligible proposition'[5], it cannot be denied that it was seen by the UK government as a vital element in the management of the NHS, and was the basis on which many of the mechanisms of a formal health planning system were established in the 1970s.

This chapter focuses on centre-periphery relationships, and looks at the way in which the UK, in particular, has attempted to resolve the dilemma of how to manage and plan a publicly provided health service while both preserving some central authority and permitting local discretion. The 'centre' is defined here as the DHSS, though it is wise to keep in mind the influence other national agencies and institutions have on the DHSS. However, this chapter is not concerned with the health policy formation process at the centre as such, but rather with the processes by which central policies are translated (or not) into local action. In order to place this discussion in context, a brief historical survey of central/local relations is first made; then the chapter considers the pattern of relations between central and local authorities, together with the various mechanisms of influence and control. The main empirical focus, however, is on the NHS and its planning system, as a case study in central-local relations.

2 THE HISTORICAL CONTEXT

The balance of power between the UK government and the NHS was frequently a source of attention before the introduction of the NHS planning system in 1976, although it was not subject to the number of in-depth investigations that, for instance, had been directed towards the relationship between central and local government. Constitutionally, the position is clear: the Secretary of State for Health and Social Services is accountable to Parliament for the operation of the NHS, and peripheral health agencies derive their authority from the centre. In practice, the relationship is more complex, leaving scope for drastically different interpretations of the balance of power. For instance, Enoch Powell, a former Minister, observed that the Regional Hospital Boards afforded the 'appearance but not the reality of dispersed initiative and judgement'[6]; whereas Richard Crossman, another Minister, saw them as 'powerful, semi-autonomous Boards whose relation to me was much more like the relations of a Persian satrap to a weak Persian Emperor'.[7] More recently, three Regional Health Authority Chairmen, having studied the DHSS and its relationship with the NHS, recommended that the DHSS should shed much of its work-load, trust its agents and force them to stand on their own feet. A review of their report commented: 'we have a national service which places all power and responsibility at the centre, and reorganisation has brought this out more clearly than before.'[8]

Paradoxically, at much the same time, there was growing public concern that the policies of the centre (especially on mental handicap and psychiatric care) were not being implemented by field authorities.[9] This view of the weakness of the centre is borne out by evidence from empirical studies on the distribution of health services and expenditure across the country. Cross-sectional analyses have indicated that inequalities are still very great, despite thirty years of a national health service dedicated to equality and equity as prime objectives.[10]

How can these various views be reconciled? Basing his work on a study of the history of the Leeds Regional Hospital Board, Ham has pointed out that the relationship between the government and the Boards appears not to have been constant over time.[11] Rather, the early years of the NHS were marked by central control, which was relaxed in the 1950s. During the 1960s, the centre and the Regions moved forward together, though the late 1960s saw increased centralisation, as a result of the enquiries into long-stay hospitals. Ham accounts for the difference of views between Powell and Crossman in the following way: 'when there was agreement at board level with departmental policy, the centre and regions moved together . . . when there was disagreement the centre had to find alternative means of imposing its will.'

Available evidence suggests that the centre both had difficulty in finding effective means of influence, and had a limited view of its own role. Two schools of thought can be discerned here. The first emphasises the perspective of the centre. Thus the seminal study by Griffith [12] described the general philosophy of the Ministry of Health as favouring the provision of advice and encouragement, rather than direction, to local health and welfare authorities. In general, he categorised the approach of the Ministry of Health as 'laissez faire'. Brown has brought this analysis more up to date[13], and noted the strengthening of the statistical, intelligence and analytical capacity of the Ministry of Health in the 1960s. None the less, he still sees the real stimulus for a change in approach to be political, stemming for instance from the use made by Crossman of public concern over conditions in long-stay hospitals to force through a more interventionist strategy.

Whereas these explanations focus on the legal powers and political will of government agencies, a second school represented by Klein[14], and more recently by Haywood and Alaszewski[15], stresses the vital influence of service deliverers on national and local decision-making. For instance, Klein affirms that 'for the State to involve itself in the control of the health service is also to make itself dependent on the co-operation of those who actually deliver the service', and concludes that the NHS conforms to a thesis of medical domination. Indeed, he argues that this power may be such that it need not openly be exercised. These commentators, therefore, do not see the structural and organisational changes that took place in 1974 as necessarily affecting central-local relations in any significant way.

The issue of the relationship between central and field authorities and the context in which a planning system is being operated thus clearly requires careful consideration. By using the UK as an illustration, and by drawing parallels with relations between government and local authorities, this issue and the prospects for its resolution can more clearly be explored.

3 MODELS OF CENTRAL/LOCAL RELATIONS

Considerable academic attention is presently being devoted to the subject of central/local relations in British local government. Models that potentially have considerable relevance to the health sector have been developed, and are being tested in a number of countries.[16] Conventional wisdom makes the distinction between an 'agency' model, where local authorities implement national policies under the supervision of central government departments and have little discretion, and a 'partnership' model, where local authorities and central departments are seen as co-equals.[17] To match this, a conventional critique has been developed, which views local authorities as political systems in their own right, making their own decisions, with central government having only the potential for control. It can be argued, however, that both approaches are one-sided, conventional wisdom focusing on legal powers, and the conventional critique on financial aspects. Instead, the variety of influences that determine the degree of local discretion need to be taken into account.

Rhodes has offered five propositions which, if valid, are likely to affect the scale of local discretion.[18] The first is the 'complex environment' in which local agencies operate, and the extent to which they are dependent on others to provide resources. In this context, resources can be financial, constitutional and legal, hierarchical, political or informational. They can vary in terms of their amount, scope ('the degree of substitutability of resources') and means ('strategies for managing resources'). Local authorities, although dependent on the centre for some financial assistance, are unlikely to be equally dependent. The degree of dependency will hinge on their access to other resources, such as political resources (ability to mobilise support) and informational resources (access to information and expertise).

The second proposition is that in order to achieve goals, organisations have to exchange resources. These goals are the product of an internal political process of negotiation and bargaining within groups, out of which emerges a dominant coalition with an agreed set of temporary goals. These goals will be constrained by the goals and decisions of other organisations (such as the government), but the dominant coalition will retain some discretion. However, the third proposition is that the 'appreciative system' of the dominant coalition will influence which relationships are seen as a problem, and what resources are sought. The appreciative system consists of interests (the stake of the individuals in the organisation), expectations (the behaviour expected of the individuals) and an ideology.

The fourth proposition is that the dominant coalition employs strategies within known 'rules of the game' to regulate the process of exchange. The rules of the game set approximate limits within which discretion may take place, and the strategies are used to gain desired resources.

The final proposition suggests that variations in the degree of discretion are a product of the goals and relative power potential of interacting organisations. This relative power potential is a product of the resources of each organisation, of the rules of the game, and of the process of exchange between organisations. Discretion will also vary according to the stage reached in the policy-making and planning process.

Rhodes summarises his propositions in the following way:

(1) variations in discretion of interacting organisations are a function of their resources, goals and relative power potential;

(2) relative power potential is the product of resources, rules of the game and the process of exchange; and the

(3) process of exchange is influenced by the resources of participants, strategies, personalities and the number of units.

In short, this approach adopts a bargaining model of centre/local relationships, and sees local agencies as political systems in their own right. It is, primarily, a suggestive, rather than explanatory model, pointing to the multiplicity of variables in that relationship, and the factors which may exert greatest influence.

The framework is reproduced at some length in this chapter, for the reader will note that it has obvious relevance to the health sector. None the less, it can be argued that there are major differences between health and local authorities in Britain. First, whereas local authorities are only partially dependent on the centre for financial resources, health authorities receive all their funds from government. Second, local authorities, as elected bodies, have a local political base, whereas health authorities are appointed, and depend on the centre for their authority. Third, the health service is strongly professionalised.

These three differences do not necessarily operate in the same direction; nor are they necessarily replicated in other countries. The first two suggest that the health authority is likely to be relatively less powerful than the local authority, while the third suggests that other factors may strengthen the health authority's position. However, these differences are not as clear-cut as they might seem, in that, despite its political base, local government is still subject to central intervention, and despite the health authority's apparent dependence, it still does have some freedom of action. In consequence, this analytical framework is of real value in looking for likely explanations for the relationship that exists between centre and periphery in the NHS.

4 MECHANISMS OF CONTROL AND INFLUENCE

The role of a health planning system in mediating between centre and periphery cannot be considered in isolation, but rather is to be seen as one part of a total system of communication and control between, and within, the various levels in the health sector. It is therefore important to consider the broad system within which any planning system must operate.

A distinction can be made here between administrative control and influence, and legislative control.[19] In any country, legislation can be mandatory and specific, or permissive and broad. In the UK, for example, health authorities have certain statutory duties (such as a duty to collaborate with the local authority); and the Secretary of State has the power, under certain circumstances, to direct or dismiss any health authority which fails to perform its duties. Statutory powers, however, tend rarely to be invoked, and central government has a formidable array of other mechanisms available, through which it can attempt to influence field authorities. Such mechanisms include:

(1) the circular – these can instruct, give general policy guidance, explain new legislation, exhort, etc.; they can be mandatory or advisory;

(2) defining major planning procedures;

(3) earmarking resources for specific purposes, thus reducing the opportunity cost of the activity to field authorities;

(4) making certain types of expenditure, such as large capital schemes and new medical manpower appointments, subject to specific, central approval; this can be a very effective means of controlling both expenditure and the nature of services;

(5) rights of appeal to the Minister, which can provide him and his department with the opportunity to influence a particular decision;

(6) carrying out centrally certain procedures, such as the negotiation of wages and salaries; and

(7) the whole range of communications - both formal and informal, at officer or Ministerial level - and flows of information, which enable the centre to keep track of local events and intervene when necessary.

Yet, for government to activate one of these mechanisms, it is dependent - at least to some extent - on the flow of timely information from field authorities. Though large quantities of statistics tend routinely to be collected, these may not provide the necessary information. Moreover, it may not be possible to see interaction solely in terms of two protagonists - centre and periphery. In Britain, as in many countries, there is an intermediate level, a Regional tier. How might this tier fit into the above discussion? Four roles appear possible for the Region: it can engage in policy-making in its own right; it can demand full involvement in implementing central policies; it can champion the cause of more peripheral authorities; or it can adopt the passive role of 'postman'.[20] Indeed, it may perform all of these roles at different times.

5 THE INTRODUCTION OF A PLANNING SYSTEM

The centre-periphery relationship and the exercise of power and control are of crucial importance when a planning system is introduced into the health sector. Two main methods are potentially available for combining accountability to the centre with the existence of some discretion at the periphery.[21] The first way is for governments to control after the event, in the light of overall performance. The second way is by establishing rules or targets in advance, for instance through a formal planning system, and holding the organisation accountable for achieving them.

In the UK, it was considered by the 1970s that the most appropriate means of achieving both delegation of authority and accountability was an interactive planning process, in which the main management control exercised by one level over the level below would consist of a continuous dialogue on policies and plans; the review and approval of plans; the appropriate allocation of resources; and the monitoring of performance against the plans. This process is portrayed diagrammatically in Figure 3. While new proposals made in 1981 imply the simplification of this process, its essential features are likely to remain unchanged. Guidelines flowed down the system, from national to local level, indicating policies, priorities and likely resource availability. Districts prepared operational plans, which were then reviewed by the Area. Similarly, Area plans (incorporating District plans) were reviewed by the Region. A report of Regional planning activities was sent annually to the DHSS, and was intended to inform and provide feedback, in order that subsequent guidelines could be amended if necessary. Once plans were approved, higher levels were expected to 'monitor' the implementation of plans by lower levels. In order to imply considerable delegation, the approval of plans

is intended only to ensure that the plan generally accords with the guidelines and contains no features to which the re•iewing Authority takes strong exception, or which are fundamentally inconsistent with other approved plans. In short, the reviewing Authority will be responsible for ensuring, not that the plan is 'right', but rather that it is not clearly wrong or inadequate.[22]

Figure 3: The Flow of Guidelines and Plans in the NHS

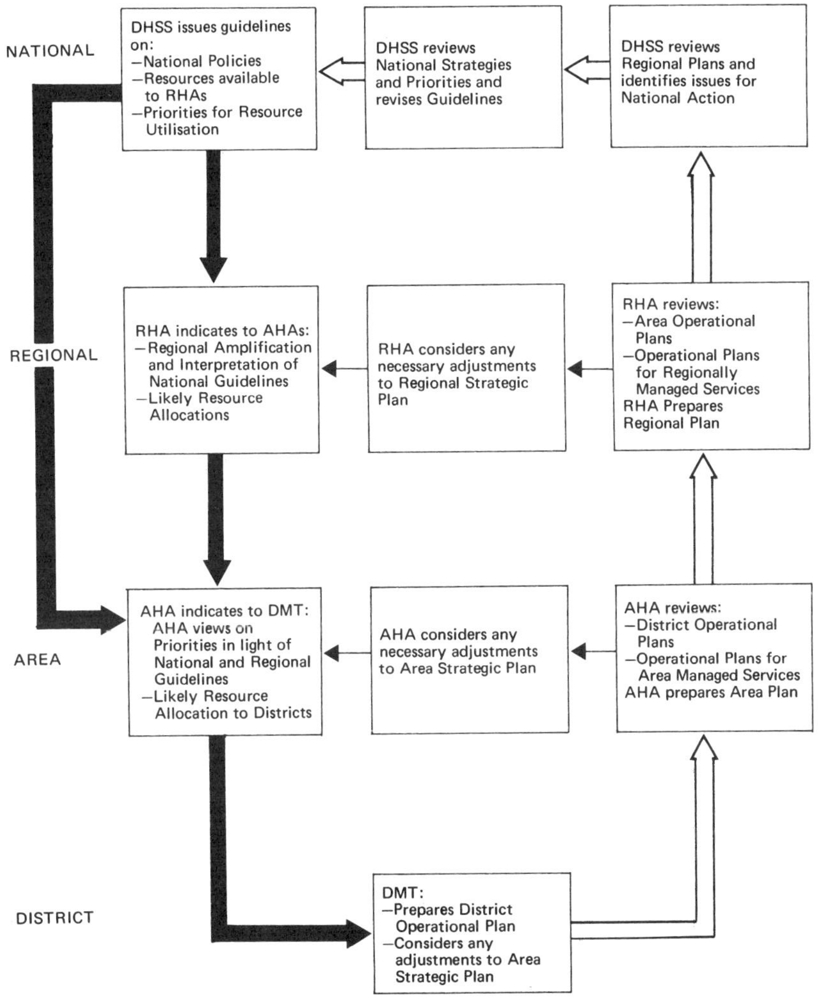

Source: DHSS, 'The NHS Planning System' (HMSO, London, 1976).

This particular form of planning system clearly implies an 'agent' model of central/local relationships where, while the centre voluntarily restricts its authority in certain respects, it does not expect its authority to be flouted openly by local agencies. However, it could be argued that such a planning system is likely to operate successfully, in terms of combining both control and planning, only if a number of conditions are met:

(1)   through the interaction of guidelines and plans, a broad consensus must emerge on the direction in which the NHS should be heading; if this does not happen, it is difficult to avoid the conclusion that the DHSS would be forced into attempting a more dictatorial role if it wishes to see its policies implemented;

(2)   field authorities should feel confident that the DHSS is responsive to their wishes, and amends its policies in the light of the feedback of local reactions; and

(3)   field authorities should be sensitive to changes in national guidance, in terms of taking note of them and ensuring they are reflected in local plans.

6   THE OPERATION OF THE NHS PLANNING SYSTEM

Introduction

In examining how planning systems have operated in practice, it is useful to make a distinction between the process of central-local relationships, and their outcomes, in terms of policy implementation. Accordingly, in the context of the UK, this section looks at the interactions of the various levels (DHSS, Region, Area, District); and at the outcomes of these interactions; and finally, at the likely balance of power between central and peripheral agencies. First, however, the section explores the concept of guidelines, for guidelines are relevant to all levels, are much emphasised in the literature and are employed frequently in communicating government policies.

The Formulation of Guidelines

When planning systems are introduced, considerable importance is often placed on guidelines as the prime mechanism that higher tiers can use to communicate their policies, influence local planning and guide before the event, rather than after. Yet there is considerable uncertainty over their content and presentation. Should they be wide-ranging, or narrow and specific; qualitative or quantitative; persuasive or mandatory?[23]

Guidelines can be divided into three main categories, depending on the force they carry:

(1)   instructions - where a central decision overrides local discretion and is supported by sanctions;

(2) exhortation - where local agencies are encouraged to adopt a particular course of action; and
(3) incentives - where a course of action is recommended and backed by extra resources.

It might be claimed that instructions are not guidelines; yet some guidelines do tend to be perceived by both centre and periphery to carry greater force than others, and to be not merely hortatory. None the less, the very word 'guidelines' suggests that most will fall into the category of 'exhortation'.

There is a strong argument for guidelines to be expressed in quantitative rather than qualitative terms, in order to provide figures against which progress can be checked. Indeed, guidelines tend frequently to rely on 'norms' of provision, which express desired levels of service in such terms as numbers of beds, numbers of staff or health centre/population ratios. Ideally, such norms should result from a priority-setting process, yet they often reflect merely average levels of present provision, or figures set by 'expert' committees at some stage in the past. While they do indeed provide a means for encouraging a measure of equality of provision across a country, and for judging the progress made by local agencies, it can also be argued that norms are often set on a flimsy basis; assume agreement on the best mix of services; focus attention on the amount of provision rather than on its use; are not necessarily appropriate or sensitive to local circumstances; and neglect local interdependencies between services.

Problems of quantification are not limited to providing recommended levels of service provision. A major task facing any type of planning is to forecast accurately the likely future availability of resources, and to provide reliable financial assumptions for local planning. The NHS planning system committed the DHSS to produce three-year and ten-year resource assumptions. Throughout the late 1970s, however, the latter were rarely given, and even the former proved unreliable in the face of public expenditure uncertainties, a changing national resource allocation policy, inflation and government changes. Moreover, the need to provide some short- and medium-term assurance on resource availability did not always accord with the government's need to be able to react flexibly to changing economic circumstances (see Chapter 9).

Ultimately, the guideline seeks to promote adherence to an overall national strategy while allowing sufficient flexibility to local agencies to adapt the details of that strategy to suit their circumstances. Yet, unless there is a common commitment at all levels to the broad objectives underpinning particular guidelines, this is unlikely to happen. Guidelines, hence, are of use so long as subsequent plans do not consistently contradict them: if they do, then sanctions may need to be used, shifting the emphasis from innovative planning to regulation, and shifting the form of guidelines from exhortation (with or without incentives) to instruction.

The DHSS Role

In the UK, the DHSS has distinguished two types of guideline: strategic guidelines on general policies, issued irregularly and remaining in force until changed; and operational guidelines, issued each year to initiate the annual planning cycle and indicate resource availability and priorities. The first two documents of strategic guidance issued after the introduction of the planning system aroused considerable interest. The first, 'Priorities for the Health and Personal Social Services'[24], was described as a 'landmark' in the history of the NHS, as the 'first attempt to devise a national strategy for the NHS and the personal social services: to translate the logic of a national service into an explicit set of targets applicable to all health authorities'.[25] Previously the DHSS had been much criticised for advocating policies without considering their resource implications. This was the first attempt in the context of service planning to determine priorities between services - to recommend, for instance, that long-stay services should be encouraged at the expense of a reduction in growth of acute services and a reduction in expenditure on maternity services.

Not surprisingly, this first document came under considerable attack not only from bodies such as the Royal College of Physicians, which called it the work of 'mathematically orientated planners', and from obstetricians, but also from those who felt it had not gone far enough.[26] None the less, if the stated purpose of the document was to provoke a debate, the publication of the second document, 'The Way Forward' [27] provided the opportunity to investigate how responsive the DHSS had proved to feedback. 'The Way Forward' stated its intention to 'continue the debate which is to become a regular exchange between central/local government, the health authorities, the professions and the staff providing these services, and the public'. As a result of comments made and representations received, the earlier strategy was modified but not essentially changed. In particular, 'The Way Forward' acknowledged that a number of factors might make rapid implementation of the strategy difficult. These included the need to meet the revenue consequences of new acute hospitals, the use made of acute services by the elderly, increases in unit costs and the need in some areas to permit rationalisation of acute services by a temporary increase in expenditure. Yet the DHSS had shown itself to be sensitive to feedback, for in the words of one commentator: 'the year 1976/7 had been spent in learning not only what was unattainable because it was unrealistic, but also what was unattainable because it was not acceptable to the health authorities and their advisers.'[28]

On the other hand, it became evident that to continue the 'debate' the DHSS required from field authorities clear information on their future plans, couched in terms that would match the national programme budget. This increasingly led the DHSS over this period to specify more closely the nature, content and form of the information flowing to it via the planning system.

Region/Area Relationships

The relationship between a Region and the Areas within it will depend on how the Region perceives its role in relation to that of central government, and how the Region perceives Area activities. According to the formal NHS planning system, the Region interpreted DHSS policy and handed it down to Areas, developed strategic plans and monitored implementation. In practice, Areas often regarded Regions with considerable antagonism. This was so in two Regions studied over a three-year period, despite differences in their approach. One Region took the lead at an early stage in strategic planning, adopting and stressing DHSS policy (which implied considerable local change), and obliging Areas to challenge Regional policy and planning in order to justify their own position. The other Region adopted a more 'bottom-up' approach, leaving Districts and Areas to prepare plans, and itself concentrating on policy statements. Yet despite what might have appeared to be a more sympathetic approach to Areas, there were still occasions when the Regional position was manifestly unwelcome, and regarded as antipathetic to Area needs and aspirations.

Here, therefore, is a 'classic' clash of roles which affects the way planning systems can operate. Regions, more aloof from day-to-day pressures, and relatively close to the national level, could afford a more distant and analytical view of local planning. Areas, in contrast, under pressure from local interest groups, were concerned to increase their autonomy, and maintain their freedom of action to cope with and accommodate the various pressures on them.

In such an environment, an important issue is the extent to which a Region can back up its guidelines by sanctions. Perhaps the most potent weapon available to Regions in the UK to influence local plans was the allocation of resources for capital developments. In contrast to revenue, which was allocated almost totally as a block grant, the Region had the authority to approve specific capital projects above a certain (relatively low) cost. Moreover, such approval could be made contingent on the development of an 'appropriate' District or Area strategy into which the specific capital project would fit. To take one example, merely by the control of capital for upgrading a hospital block, one Region was able to alter a local decision, taken after a very lengthy local debate, on the location of maternity services for a District. The volte-face forced on the Area and District presented them with almost insurmountable problems in soothing those whose interests had been adversely affected by the Region's actions.

Indeed, the flow of guidelines and plans between Region and Area could be seen not so much as a consensus-forming process, but rather as a process of negotiation, bargaining and compromise, through which a modus vivendi on particular issues was reached. This can again be illustrated by reference to a long-running debate in one Area over the numbers of local acute beds needed. The Region insisted the Area should plan to reduce its beds to the national norm by the end of the ten-year planning period; the Area maintained that its local circumstances were such as to require the retention of a higher norm. Over a three- to four-year period of frequent bargaining and discussion, a final figure was agreed, higher than the Region's figure. This result can be attributed to the degree of mutual dependence between the two Authorities. The success of the Regional strategy was dependent on the release of resources from the Area by the reduction in acute hospital beds. The Region was, therefore, dependent on the Area's co-operation. At the same time, since the Area was dependent on the Region for capital resources, it could not afford to adopt a clearly unrealistic bargaining posture, though it could, and did, summon up data and analysis to support its arguments.

Area/District Relationships

It is an apt illustration of the impact of relationships between tiers on planning that while, in the debate referred to above, the Area was arguing with the Region for the mitigation of the Regional strategy, and maintaining its need for the resources it consumed, it was at the same time insisting locally to its Districts that there was some slack in acute services that could be transferred to deprived services. Indeed, the Area role was perhaps the most difficult in the reorganised NHS structure, since it was forced to mediate between the Region, which could afford to be aloof from day-to-day pressures, and the District, which could justify its role by reference to the day-to-day management of services.

With hindsight, the role of the Area and its power to effect change was weak. Indeed, the Area level is to be removed in a second NHS reorganisation, and few dissenting voices have been raised to this particular proposal. Various reasons can be suggested for the weakness of the Area level. The operational feasibility of any proposal had to be judged by the District and the Area lacked the detailed knowledge of the service to contradict it; the District, to maintain the operation of services, had to be sensitive to local pressures, and these could outweigh any pressures the Area could bring to bear; although the Area was the level of statutory authority, Districts could advise the Area Health Authority directly without going through Area officers; and a number of the members of the AHA sympathised with Districts rather than with the Area. Furthermore, the influence of the Area was weakened because it had limited powers, in contrast to the Region, to arbitrate on local decisions or approve new developments. In short, there was little Areas could promise Districts on their own authority, and their influence was only partially strengthened by the desire of Districts to have Areas as their allies in arguments with Regions.

Adherence to National Policy

An indication of the balance of power in the centre-periphery relationship is given by the extent to which the flow of national guidelines leads to the implementation of developments in conformity with national strategies. The outcome of the dialogue between the tiers can be illustrated by reference to two Areas studied in depth.

Both Areas appeared to agree with the broad strategies propounded by the DHSS; the main issue, however, was the extent to which this philosophical agreement was translated into action. To take in turn examples of the three categories of instructions, incentives and exhortation, resource assumptions, as an example of instructions, were treated with great respect in one Area, and with some respect in the other. In both Areas, however, the degree of force carried by the assumptions was weakened by their variability. Moreover, in the second Area, operational plans tended to adopt higher resource assumptions as a negotiating ploy, and strategic plans proposed a 'realistic' level of provision, tempered but not totally constrained by resource assumptions.

The provision of centrally determined financial incentives increased the likelihood that policies would be followed, but did not guarantee conformity. For instance, while earmarked capital resources for health centres were attractive, various local barriers to the successful establishment of a health centre could prove a more serious constraint than finance. Consideration of the experience of joint finance in Chapter 8 provides a similar lesson. It is clear, therefore, that what may appear at national level as an incentive may not always appear in the same light at local level, when matched against the other opportunities and constraints faced by field authorities.

While norms and targets fall within the category 'exhortation', in practice some were extremely influential while others were ignored. The norms taken most seriously were those linked to the approval of capital projects, in the sense that major capital developments were granted only if plans adhered to national or regional bed norms. Norms could, in particular circumstances, thus be given considerable weight, though there was usually some scope for negotiation.

Overall, it could be claimed that a measure of agreement on future developments was reached between the tiers over the three years studied. In one Area, the continuing dialogue on plans appeared to be leading to a consensus. In the other Area, the discussion process could more appropriately be described as negotiation, leading to compromises, with many points of disagreement not resolved: consensus would appear to be an inappropriate term, except at a very high level of generalisation. None the less, the planning system had given rise to a dialogue, and in this latter Area at least, to an agreement that change in the direction of national priorities was necessary. Change, however, proved extraordinarily difficult to achieve. For instance, an investigation of the development of mental handicap policy over the 1970s in one of the Areas showed that the Area was anxious to follow DHSS guidelines and, indeed, produced many plans. Yet little progress was made in implementation, largely because the extra resources needed could come only from redeployment, and mental handicap was not given priority over other programmes. This issue of the implementation of plans is vital. A planning system may produce well developed plans, but these are futile unless they lead to action.

The Balance of Power

It would appear from the above evidence that there is no simple answer to the question of whether the NHS planning system has led to greater central influence, and that the picture on whether 'delegation downwards and accountability upwards' have been achieved is also very unclear. It has been possible to detect a tendency, at Regional and national levels, to employ means which imply greater centralisation, while Areas, but especially Districts, have by virtue of their location and responsibilities been able to protect considerably their freedom of action. The UK scene, in consequence, has been one of considerable tension and conflict between the levels of the health service, rather different from the smooth-running system originally envisaged.

How can this be explained? The NHS planning system assumed the NHS to be a well controlled, hierarchical organisation with general agreement on means and goals. But as discussed in Chapters 3 and 4, the provision of health care involves so many bodies, each with its own interests, that a seemingly 'well designed' policy, even matched by resources, will not be sufficient to ensure implementation if it runs counter to the motivations, rewards and penalties of the institutions and individuals that must carry it out.[29] Of these groups, those that have appeared most significant locally in recent times have been the medical profession, trade unions and the public. Managers and health authorities have had always to keep the demands and opinions of these groups in mind when considering the extent to which national policy was relevant and could be implemented.

The contribution of these various groups to local planning, and the ways in which they could influence planning decisions, are considered in the next chapter. It needs to be said here, however, that their influence is by no means neutral with respect to which policies are acceptable locally. The balance of power within the medical profession favours the acute, high-technology specialties and the teaching hospitals. Thus those services to which the DHSS has attempted to give priority over a number of years are precisely those whose status within the medical profession is lowest. On the other hand, various local pressure groups exist which do campaign for priority to be given to care groups such as the elderly, disabled and handicapped, and do so the more strongly because of the moral support they derive from DHSS priorities.

To express these features in conceptual terms, the increasing influence of a variety of different bodies on government and public agencies can be described as the 'diffusion' of power.[30] Negative power, the power to prevent change, is widespread amongst groups such as doctors and ancillary workers. Yet no similar tangible influence, or positive power, exists in the hands of any one group to create change in the same direct and immediate way. Change is thus possible only by obtaining the consent and co-operation of a variety of local groups, by means of a 'negotiated order'. It would be misleading, however, to see order being negotiated unconstrained by forces outside the locality. The Region and DHSS do have a very real authority, even though they also must recognise the nature of the local environment of the health service. An Area Health Authority was suspended in 1979 for failing to keep its level of expenditure within defined limits, and this must have acted as a warning to other Areas that ultimately there were central controls on their activities. While the Minister's action was later judged unlawful, the ruling challenged his choice of strategies of intervention, not his right to intervene.[31]

This point raises an important constitutional issue. While the DHSS has aspired to use the planning system to devolve decision-making, the capacity of the Area Health Authority, as the lowest statutory authority, to support that devolution can be questioned. Although it is statutorily accountable to the Regional Health Authority, the Area Health Authority possesses members (from local authorities and staff organisations) whose prime allegiance lies elsewhere. Indeed, it is an extraordinarily heterogeneous body, with members of very different backgrounds and experience. Moreover, it is voluntary and part-time, and is thus in a weak position to challenge the decisions made by the management teams of officers. Yet the ability of these teams themselves to cope effectively with decision-making and to control the activities of professional staff has been called into question by several well publicised management failures.[32] The replacement of Area Health Authorities by District Health Authorities in 1982 is likely to leave these basic issues largely unaffected.

A dilemma is thus posed for the planning system by the structure of the NHS. While the planning system has been formulated to encourage decentralisation, in practice the structure is such that accountability for local decision-making is weak. Yet the authority of the DHSS is rarely openly flouted, and it is important to note that only one Authority has carried its dislike of financial restrictions to the point of openly challenging government policy. This would seem to indicate the importance of two features: first, the strict central control over financial aspects and local acceptance of its legitimacy; and second, the very much looser control the DHSS exercises over policies and priorities, especially where these relate to medical matters. Thus while the DHSS is prepared to exert its authority in the financial sphere, policies and priorities are left more to the discretion of peripheral authorities, and are largely the subject of exhortation rather than of direction. The exceptions, and they are very much exceptions, occur only when particular incidents make it necessary and legitimate for the DHSS to take a more dominant role.

7 DETERMINANTS OF LOCAL DISCRETION

It will by now be evident that the complexities of the NHS are such that it is difficult to come to any general conclusions on the nature and determinants of central/local relationships, and on the extent of local discretion. This task is, however, helped by the application of Rhodes' propositions on local discretion introduced at the beginning of this chapter, namely the availability of resources, the need to achieve goals, the local appreciative system and the strategies adopted.

In the first place, it might seem that the legal position of peripheral authorities, and their dependence on higher authorities for resources, should in practice leave little room for local discretion. However, most resources are allocated in the form of a block grant, and the field authority controls the production, and to some extent the form, of the information that indicates to higher tiers what is happening. The appropriate use of data, analysis and expertise to support local arguments can also promote local discretion. Moreover, Areas may be able to mobilise political support (amongst the community, trade unions, local authorities, local Members of Parliament) which can help to counterbalance higher authority, and local compliance (especially of the medical profession) is a crucial condition for implementation.

The goals of each Area, as is clear from this chapter, are a product of many different pressures. The DHSS and Regions are a source of significant pressure, but the pressures wielded by some local groups can be as significant. The interdependencies within the whole system of health care are such that an Area's goals are inevitably constrained by those of other organisations.

Yet the appreciative system means that not all relationships are seen as a source of major conflict. For instance, an ideology common to many NHS administrators incorporates recognition of the NHS as a national organisation and ascribes considerable authority to DHSS pronouncements. In particular, observance of financial regulations and good financial management are considered of great importance, and the promotion of policies and priorities is considered a legitimate central function. Local opposition seldom condemns central policies as such, but rather their local relevance. DHSS authority, in consequence, is rarely openly challenged. The authority of the Region, in contrast, is not considered as valid to the same extent by officers in lower tiers. In general, managers attach great weight to the view of the medical profession, and the right of Community Health Councils, local community groups and local authorities to have their views taken into account is much less widely accepted. None the less, the introduction of CHCs and the influence of local authorities on the Area Health Authority mean that in some instances the traditional appreciative system of deference to the DHSS is coming increasingly under attack, and a greater emphasis is being placed on the need for local discretion. Hence, and perhaps paradoxically, while the planning system can lead to greater centralism, it can also be used by these newer influences to promote local autonomy.

The form and content of strategies adopted to influence the allocation of resources vary between tiers and between Areas. Inevitably, the strategies adopted depend on the powers of the tier. Thus the DHSS can resort to earmarking, and the Region to the control of capital. None the less, there are 'rules of the game' which set limits to behaviour; thus over-expenditure is not, on the whole, seen as an appropriate tactic, nor overt mobilisation by managers of local political support against the policies of higher levels.

It should now be clear from the above discussion why it is difficult to come to any general conclusions on the centre-local relationship in the NHS. The relationship will vary by tier; by geographical area; depending on what the centre or any particular locality wishes to achieve; depending on what resources - political support or informed analysis and expertise - authorities can bring to bear; and depending on what expectations they have, and which individuals are involved. The planning system is thus operating in an extremely complex environment, where communications between the tiers tend to take the form of bargaining, and local health authorities do not act as mere 'agents' of central government.

8 CONCLUSION: IMPLICATIONS FOR PLANNING SYSTEMS

Are there lessons to be learnt from this analysis of the relationship between central and peripheral agencies within the NHS which are relevant to health policy-making and planning in other countries? At least four main lessons can be distinguished: on the use of guidelines; on matching planning systems to organisational behaviour; on the use of sanctions; and on the danger of using planning systems for control purposes.

Many planning systems place considerable emphasis on using the mechanism of guidelines to shape local plans. Yet considerable thought needs to be given to formulating central guidance in ways relevant to and comprehensible at local level. Moreover, a realistic appraisal of guidelines would perceive them as exhortatory, rather than as instructions carrying some force. In contrast, plans are likely to· carry much greater weight and commitment, and thus to stimulate more comment and argument. None the less, both guidelines and plans can serve as the means for communications and negotiations on future developments between the levels of a health system.

Planning systems will usually be introduced into a previously existing health system, where particular patterns of behaviour and relationships are well established. The existence of a number of levels in the health system may lead to rivalry, bargaining and tensions between the levels. This is likely to affect their planning behaviour: for instance, lower levels may choose to ignore central resource guidelines for planning, and instead exaggerate their resource demands, as their 'opening bid' for central resources. Thus the architects of planning systems must consider the existing nature of centre-periphery relationships, and tailor the planning system appropriately.

Given that the objectives of each level will not necessarily coincide, a crucial issue for each tier is what sanctions it can bring to bear to support its own guidelines and policies, and attempt to ensure they are implemented. Since capital, and to a lesser extent manpower, are often allocated by higher levels in response to local bids for projects (rather than allocated as a block grant), these then become the prime tools that higher levels can use to shape local developments. Such sanctions (or incentives) have important implications for any planning system, for they concentrate attention on capital projects and medical manpower, rather than on service planning and health care.

Finally, the effect of trying to use a planning system both as a system of control and as a mechanism for developing ideas on future strategies requires careful consideration. Many would argue that a planning system should permit flexibility, to allow for uncertainties and changing circumstances, and should encourage innovative and creative thinking. Yet the NHS experience shows that the danger of making a planning system also a system of control is that higher levels will attempt to use it to prescribe local activities, and control behaviour rigidly, thus causing local frustration with planning.

However, it would be a mistake to assume that a nationalised health system such as the NHS must necessarily be monolithic and over-centralised.[33] Certainly, governments do aim to shape and constrain the behaviour of their peripheral health agencies, but their ability to control local behaviour in detail is likely always to be limited. Indeed, many of the failures to implement government policy can be ascribed to the lack of comprehension at national level of local values, perceptions and motivations. Some discretion at the periphery is essential; the problem is how to reconcile this with accountability to higher political levels. On the one hand, it is a matter of how far central government can go, ought to go, and indeed, is prepared to go in deciding national priorities and ensuring their implementation at the local level. On the other hand, it is a matter of how far local groups will sacrifice their institutional arrangements and commitments to comply with national guidelines and policies, and thereby ensure their plans are funded.

NOTES

1. R. G. S. Brown, 'The Management of Welfare' (Fontana, London, 1975).
2. E. Craven (ed.), 'Regional Devolution and Social Policy' (Macmillan, London, 1975).
3. J. P. Vaughan and A. Mills, 'Area Health Management and Support for Primary Health Care' (mimeo., Ross Institute, London, 1981).
4. DHSS, 'Management Arrangements for the Reorganised National Health Service' (HMSO, London, 1972).
5. W. J. M. Mackenzie, 'Power and Responsibility in Health Care' (Oxford University Press, Oxford, 1979).
6. J. E. Powell, 'Medicine and Politics: 1975 and After' (Pitman Medical, Tunbridge Wells, 1976).
7. R. H. S. Crossman, 'A Politician's View of Health Service Planning' (The University of Glasgow, Glasgow, 1972).
8. Hospital and Health Services Review, Editorial, A Slimline DHSS? 'Hospital and Health Services Review', vol. 72, no. 10 (October 1976).
9. J. Turner, No Votes, No Hopes, 'New Society', 26 April 1979.
10. J. H. Rickard, Per Capita Expenditure of the English Area Health Authorities, 'British Medical Journal', 31

January 1976.
11. C. Ham, 'Policy-Making in the NHS' (Macmillan, London, 1981).
12. J. A. G. Griffith, 'Central Departments and Local Authorities' (George Allen and Unwin, London, 1966).
13. R. G. S. Brown, 'Reorganising the NHS: a Case Study of Administrative Change' (Basil Blackwell and Martin Robertson, Oxford, 1979).
14. R. Klein, The Corporate State, the Health Service and the Professions, 'New Universities Quarterly', vol. 31, no. 2 (1977), pp. 161-80.
15. S. Haywood and A. Alaszewski, 'Crisis in the Health Service: the Politics of Management' (Croom Helm, London, 1980).
16. M. Goldsmith, Central-Local Government Relations in Different Countries, 'SSRC Newsletter', no. 43 (March 1981).
17. F. Layfield, 'Local Government Finance', Report of the Committee of Enquiry (HMSO, London, 1976).
18. R. A. W. Rhodes, Research into Central-Local Relations in Britain: a Framework for Analysis in SSRC, 'Central-Local Government Relationships' (Social Science Research Council, London, 1979).
19. J. Stanyer, 'Understanding Local Government' (Fontana, London, 1976).
20. School for Advanced Urban Studies, Implementation and the Central-Local Relationship in SSRC, 'Central-Local Government Relationships'.
21. R. G. S. Brown, Accountability and Control in the NHS, 'Hospital and Health Services Review', Centre 8 Pages (1977).
22. DHSS, 'The NHS Planning System' (HMSO, London, 1976).
23. A. J. Mills and J. Reynolds, Centre-Periphery: Can Guidelines Bridge the Gap? 'Hospital and Health Services Review' (February 1977).
24. DHSS, 'Priorities for the Health and Personal Social Services' (HMSO, London, 1976).
25. R. Klein, Priorities and the Problems of Planning, 'British Medical Journal', 22 October 1977.
26. Radical Statistics Health Group, 'Whose Priorities?' (1977).
27. DHSS, 'The Way Forward' (HMSO, London, 1977).
28. Brown, Accountability and Control.
29. K. Lee, Health Care: Planning, Policies and Incentives, 'Futures' (December 1979), pp. 482-90.
30. J. Straw, 'Power in Government - a Chinese Puzzle' (Convocation Lecture, Leeds University, 1978).
31. Law Report, Minister's hospital directions based on misleading advice, 'The Times', 26 February 1980.
32. Haywood and Alaszewski, 'Crisis in the Health Service', p. 103.
33. K. Lee, Public Expenditure, Health Services and Health

in A. Walker (ed.), 'Public Expenditure and Social Priorities' (Heinemann, London, 1981).

7 LOCAL INTEREST GROUPS AND THE PLANNING PROCESS

1 INTRODUCTION

In the previous chapter, consideration was given to the impact of the relationships between central and peripheral health authorities on the determination and implementation of health policies. In particular, the chapter suggested that various local groups, both external and internal to health service authorities, might wield sufficient power to impede the implementation of national policies. Indeed, health planning systems in, for instance, the US and UK make explicit provision for the expression or even assertion of the views held by particular interest groups such as the community, professional staff and ancillary workers.

This chapter investigates the local relationships of health authorities in more detail, focusing in particular on the involvement of these groups in policy-making and planning. It explores the possible mechanisms and procedures for participation and consultation, which groups may be involved, how influential they can be, and how a planning process such as that in the UK can cope with pressure for group involvement. Since terms such as 'participation' and 'consultation' have been used in various ways, the chapter first looks at their meaning. It then considers the rationale for involving various groups in the decision-making process, explores which groups seem to have a legitimate place and discusses the factors that are important in affecting their ability to influence decisions. The experience of the British NHS in inviting and coping with these processes is then investigated. Finally, the chapter concludes with some remarks about the ways in which interest groups have been involved in NHS planning, and how best planning structures can be designed to incorporate and cope with the demands made on them by such groups.

The cultural context of this (and the following) chapter is primarily Britain and the US. Any planning system, however, needs to tackle the issue of the extent to which groups from, for instance, communities and professions should be involved in the planning process, and how this can best be achieved.

2 THE MEANING OF INVOLVEMENT

Terms such as participation, consultation, negotiation and informing are frequently used to describe the 'involvement' of various individuals and groups in decision-making. It is therefore vital to establish, at the very outset, an understanding of the way in which these various terms are used in this chapter. One of the most frequently quoted sets of definitions is the terminology developed by Arnstein [1] who has, within the context of the US, set out a 'ladder of citizen participation' as follows:

Citizen Control
Delegated Power
Partnership

Placation
Consultation
Informing

Therapy
Manipulation

These categories are intended to be provocative and only the first three represent degrees of citizen power. The implication of the first, 'citizen control', is clear; with 'delegated power', citizens have dominant decision-making authority and a veto; for 'partnership', power is redistributed through negotiation. The next three terms represent degrees of tokenism: 'placation' exists where a few citizens are placed on executive boards, or citizen advisory committees are created without being given power; 'consultation' provides no assurance that citizen views will be taken into account and 'informing' may provide no channels for the feedback of views, though both may be important steps towards participation. The final two categories, representing non-participation, are 'therapy', where for instance citizens are 'educated' to adopt 'correct' views, and 'manipulation', where citizens are placed on rubber-stamp advisory bodies.

An alternative classification system is that offered by Ham.[2] His list of forms of public participation comprises:

(1) negotiation: a group's views are sought and the decision is contingent on that group's approval;
(2) consultation: a group's views are actively sought and may or may not be taken into account;
(3) public relations: a group's views are sought but in such a way as to rule out influence over decision-making; and
(4) articulation: a group presents views without these being sought.

In comparing the merits of these two sets of definitions, a basic issue is whether definitions should be concerned directly with the degree of influence on decision-making, or whether they should merely describe forms of involvement. Ham argues, in terms of his definitions, that while the form of involvement and the amount of power exercised by a group are obviously linked, there is no necessary correlation between them. Arnstein, in contrast, bases her typology on the degree of power wielded by citizens.

In this chapter, the aim is to consider how a planning process can incorporate the views of various groups in planning, and cope with the power of some groups to dominate other groups and ensure that their own interests are taken into account in the decision-making process. In some ways, however, giving the chapter this focus on planning as a process of arbitrating between groups with different degrees of power does not help the task of definition, since the concept of 'power' is elusive. Lukes [3] has defined power as 'A exercises power over B when A affects B in a manner contrary to B's interests', and notes that power can be viewed in terms of three dimensions, reflecting approaches which he terms conflict-centred, conflict avoidance and the 'unconscious' exercise of power.

The conflict-centred approach, termed by Lukes the 'one-dimensional' view, sets out to study specific outcomes in order to determine whose will has prevailed in community decision-making. In particular, the approach analyses issues involving actual, observable conflict. However, by so doing, it largely ignores the use of power and influence in those instances where conflict is absent, and also rejects the possibility that interests may be unvoiced or unobservable, or that people may be mistaken about or unaware of their own interests.

The conflict avoidance approach, or 'two-dimensional' view, accepts that power may be wielded unconsciously, and recognises also that power can embrace coercion, influence, authority, force and manipulation.[4] This view argues that a study of the avoidance of conflict or 'a decision that results in the suppression or thwarting of a latent or manifest challenge to the values or interests of the decision-maker' may be as important as looking at actual conflict.

Lukes has criticised this second approach on the following grounds. First, he has suggested that it gives a misleading picture of the way power is expected to exclude issues from the political process: exclusion may not follow from conscious choice, or be an intended result. Second, the exclusion of issues is not simply the result of individual choice, but also of the socially structured and culturally patterned behaviour of groups and practices of institutions. Third, the approach associates power with actual, observable conflict, whereas 'manipulation' and 'authority' may prevent conflict from arising in the first place, by shaping wants and preventing grievances. Lukes, therefore, stresses the importance of a third dimension, namely the 'unconscious' exercise of power.

If one accepts this analysis of power and applies it to the notion of 'involvement', it appears that full involvement in decision-making cannot exist so long as one group is able to exercise power, consciously or unconsciously, over another group involved in the decision-making process. Instead, lesser degrees of involvement such as placation, consultation and informing are likely to persist. Where there is full involvement, then this implies shared decision-making, probably established through negotiation. Yet if power is exercised unconsciously, whether or not full involvement is taking place in any particular set of circumstances will be difficult to establish.

A working set of definitions of involvement in decision-making can now be established, at least for the purposes of this chapter. The terms which are used frequently (and often loosely) to describe the 'involvement' of various bodies in the planning process are collaboration, participation, consultation and negotiation. These are now defined as follows.

(1) Collaboration implies that the organisations or groups in question have equal rights to be involved in the formulation of each other's goals and in their achievement where these are matters of mutual responsibility, concern and interest. In other words, collaboration implies shared decision-making by equal partners with overlapping responsibilities.

(2) Participation implies that representatives of interest groups actively take part in the decision-making processes, and have equal power to affect the outcome. In other words, participation implies shared decision-making by equal partners, but without necessarily all participating groups having responsibility for the area of interest.

(3) Consultation is the seeking of advice, information or opinion, without a commitment to follow views received, and with the consulting body responsible for the final decision.

(4) Negotiation takes place where one body cannot get what it wants without seeking an accommodation with another party.

It should be noted that this terminology does not follow those writers for whom, for instance, participation is the generic term, and consultation a form of participation. Rather, both are used in this chapter as forms of involvement.

3 THE CASE FOR GROUP INVOLVEMENT

Many countries have shown, in recent years, growing interest in seeking ways of involving citizens and workers in the preparation of public sector plans. In Britain, for instance, when many public sector activities were scrutinised and reorganised during the 1960s and 1970s, often in a search for economies of scale, increasing scope was also being given for the opinions of consumers of public sector services to be voiced. At the same time, there was a similar, though much less strong, trend in the public sector for worker participation, that is to involve all those working within the organisation in its direction and operation.

Workers and consumers represent only two of the various groups, both inside and outside the health sector, which may be involved in one form or another in health planning and policy-making. For the purposes of this chapter it is useful to distinguish five broad categories of groups, each of which in countries such as Britain potentially represents a competing influence on planning. The first group is that of health professionals, defined to include all those professions working within the health sector. The second, the community, encompasses the various groups which claim to represent community and consumer views, whether on the whole health system or a particular service. The third covers labour interests (excluding the professions) and the fourth those organisations whose activities have an impact on, or are affected by, the health sector. The final category, the managers of the health service or the bureaucrats, represents in one sense a distinct group of interests; in another sense it consists of the arbiters of the planning process, who thus influence the extent to which the other categories of interest groups are actually involved in planning. Each of these categories could, of course, be broken down into a number of sub-groups.

Why should there be this increasing enthusiasm to involve these various groups, or at least some of them, in planning?[5] Three arguments in favour of group involvement can be discerned. Some proponents believe in a 'participatory theory of democracy.'[6] They stress that maximum participation is necessary for democracy, and that it is a means of self-education in public matters, thus implying that such involvement will not threaten the stability of political systems. It follows that participation should take place at all levels, not only nationally but also in local communities, the workplace and in social organisations.

Second, others see participation as a means of redressing the balance of power between the people and government.[7] Their analyses focus on the inadequacy and episodic nature of the information on citizens' dissatisfactions reaching governments. They stress that the solution lies not in generating more information, since the decision-maker will listen only to those sources which matter to him, but in adjusting the balance of power, thus forcing the interests and knowledge of citizens on governments.

A third reason given for participation is to improve the quality of decisions and to assist the implementation of plans, on the assumption that those participating in drawing up plans will then be committed to implementing them. Thus Emery [8] has suggested: 'The more knowledge the expert accumulates, the greater the gap between him and the people, and the less likely they are to go along with helping to implement his plans.' This writer stresses the problems posed by a complex and constantly changing environment, and considers that these can be dealt with only by seeing planning as a participative 'search process' for discovering ideals common to the main parties to a proposed change, and designing a 'change process' which enables learning and constant adaptation to take place as change proceeds. This rationale can also be seen in other documents such as those which recommend public participation in planning in order to improve the quality of public sector decision-making and to give personal satisfaction to those likely to be affected by plans.[9]

Although these various writers unite in advocating participation, it is clear that they do not all have the same conception of participation. Nor, by implication, do they all ascribe the same degree of power to the various groups. Indeed, a number of factors can be discerned that, in practice, will influence the power of each of the groups.[10] In the first place, the prevailing political culture will set the limits for interest group activity. Thus, in different societies, there will be different expectations of appropriate activities and different norms of behaviour that will define the way in which interest groups should behave. Second, the potential power of each group will depend on the organisational characteristics of the body inviting involvement. These characteristics will include the attitudes of decision-makers and the degree of involvement they wish to permit, and the management and planning procedures which can either facilitate or impede involvement.[11] Elected decision-makers may see no reason to involve the public on a continuing basis, and managers and professionals may feel that their expertise equips them to make decisions without the direct involvement of others. For instance, expert planners and sophisticated planning systems may effectively preclude the citizen 'from the right to participate in those "technical" decisions'.[12] Third, the organisational characteristics of the groups themselves will affect their power to influence decisions. These characteristics will include their resources (in terms of money, skills and advice), their prestige, their legitimacy (in particular their status at law and statutory powers), their size, organisational cohesiveness and political skills.[13]

131

Is it possible to come to any general conclusion on the conditions and circumstances in which the involvement of interested parties in planning is likely to lead to an exchange of views felt to be fruitful, and to decisions that are accepted by all parties? Perhaps one should first ask the question, are people or groups naturally inclined to desire involvement in health planning and policy-making? The answer obtained will depend on their perception (which will vary from person to person) of the costs and benefits to them of involvement. These costs and benefits will include the effort and time necessary to become involved, the monetary costs of so doing, the stake individuals or groups have in the decision, their valuation of the importance of a favourable decision, and of the chances of getting it. The greater the divergence between expectations of benefits and results, the more frustrating the process is likely to be. And the fewer the opportunities for individuals to become involved in decisions that affect them, whether made by national or local governments, in the community or in the workplace, the more difficult it is likely to be to stimulate public or group interest in one particular sector such as health.

To see how well these arguments explain reality, the following sections look at the way in which interest groups are involved in health planning, that is at possible structural and procedural arrangements. The health service planning system in the UK is taken as the example, and the UK experience is then examined in terms of the extent to which the expectations of all those involved in health planning were met, and also in terms of the impact different groups had on the decision-making process. The chapter concludes with comments on the way in which a planning system can provide the opportunity for, and cope with, the involvement of various interests.

4 THE UK HEALTH PLANNING SYSTEM: A CASE STUDY OF GROUP INVOLVEMENT

Both the structure of the NHS and its planning system take into account the existence of interest groups in a variety of ways. In order to understand later discussion on the extent of their involvement in planning, it is first necessary to detail the structural and procedural arrangements surrounding their involvement.

Structural Arrangements

During the 1970s, the Area Health Authority (AHA) in England had formal statutory responsibility for managing the local health service. However, its members were appointed by virtue of their involvement with particular organisations or professions, such as local authorities and the medical and nursing professions, or of their status in the community. Their ultimate claim to membership may therefore be seen to rest on three quite different principles - the popular vote, syndicalism and patronage - giving rise to three clusters of potential interests, of elected, professional and appointed members.[14] It should be said that, formally, members were expected to attend in their own right, and not as representatives of these sectional interests. Whether this was a reasonable expectation can be questioned.

This distinction between members acting in their own right and not as representatives of their parent organisations was considered important, for separate structures existed to encourage co-operation between the health service and related organisations such as the local authority. These took various forms, for instance Joint Consultative Committees, Planning Teams, Liaison Committees and <u>ad hoc</u> joint groups established locally. This chapter concentrates on the involvement of community interests and 'worker' interests, broadly defined. Collaboration with other organisations, in particular the local authority, is briefly reviewed here, but detailed consideration, in view of the importance of the topic, is deferred to the next chapter.

Involvement by the public in the NHS can, in general, be defined in such a way as to include any means by which people at large can affect the operation and planning of health services. Such a definition would encompass the activities of local pressure groups, the electorate's collective voice speaking through Parliament and the activities of local government councillors as elected local representatives.[15] However, the structure for community involvement in the NHS has been of particular interest, for since 1974 a specific body, the Community Health Council (CHC), has had the task of expressing the views of the community. Not surprisingly, this has not prevented groups within the community adopting other means of making their voices heard.

Each CHC, with responsibility for one Health District, was intended to

> provide a new means of representing the local community's interests in the health services to those responsible for managing them. In the reorganised NHS, management of the service and representation of local opinion will be distinct but complementary functions, entrusted to separate bodies but working in close relationship.[16]

None the less, the original composition of CHCs suggested an attempt had been made to hold a balance between various interests, for half of the members were appointed by the local authority (and did not need to be councillors) and the rest were elected by appropriate voluntary bodies, or appointed by the Regional Health Authority.[17]

DHSS pronouncements gave CHCs a potentially important role in the planning system. An AHA was legally obliged to consult CHCs on 'any proposals which it may have under consideration for any substantial development of the health service in the Council's District and on proposals to make any substantial variation in the provision of such a service'[18] and this was re-emphasised later by the advice that CHCs should be consulted at the earliest possible stage.[19] Correspondingly, the CHC had a duty to advise on the operation of the health service, and to make recommendations for its improvement. Subsequently, the CHC's power, if only the power to delay, was strengthened further by allowing a right of appeal to the Secretary of State if a CHC disagreed with an AHA proposal to close a hospital. However, the CHC was obliged to make a detailed and constructive counter-proposal, taking into account the AHA's reasons for proposing closure.

Not surprisingly, the advent of CHCs has led to a considerable academic debate [20] about the extent to which they can be termed 'representative' of the community when they are neither elected by, nor typical of, the community; on their power to influence the AHA; and on the extent to which they are liable to be manipulated or co-opted by management.

Considering next the NHS professions, and in particular the medical profession, their independence and autonomy make the NHS virtually unique among organisations. One of the principles basic to the reorganisation of the health service in 1974 was that:

> The health care professions should be integrally involved in planning and management at all levels. This involvement must be achieved without infringing the clinical autonomy of medical and dental consultants and general practitioners, and without interfering with the professional standards of the health care professions or inhibiting the exercise of professional judgement by members of those professions.[21]

The structural mechanisms for involving the medical profession were manifold.[22] Below District level there existed a system of committees for involving professional staff in management; and professional staff were invited to participate in District Planning Teams, set up to review the health needs of particular care groups. At District level, the District Medical Committee (elected by all doctors in the District) had both advisory and executive roles, in addition electing two representatives to the District Management Team to share in its duties and responsibilities, including control of the operational planning cycle and determination of the content of the annual plan. At Area and Regional levels there were professional advisory committees for doctors (and often for particular clinical specialties) and for other professions, and members of the medical and nursing professions were appointed to the AHA and RHA.

In contrast, the formal mechanisms for the involvement of ancillary workers in planning and policy determination were far less elaborate and complete. During the 1970s, the DHSS espoused the principle of participative management, which it defined as 'a method of enabling more staff in the NHS to become involved in changing for the better the way they work'.[23] This was to be achieved by improved communications between management and staff, and by the establishment of joint working groups and Joint Staff Committees to consider operational problems.[24]

Procedural Arrangements

The above section has set out how the various interest groups were embodied or represented in the reorganised structure of the NHS, and has indicated the planning role thought appropriate to each of them. Three stages for their involvement can now be distinguished: in the formulation of planning proposals, through formal consultation on plans and in the approval of proposals and plans.

The formulation of planning proposals was intended to be primarily the responsibility of District Planning Teams (DPTs), made up largely of NHS staff, but also including local authority officers and possibly CHC members. These various interest groups were therefore indirectly involved in the formulation process, and DPTs were instructed to formulate proposals in the light of the known views of the CHC, local authority and other local bodies. Formal consultation (normally on operational and strategic plans, but also on specific change of use or closure proposals) was to be conducted with a wide range of different organisations and groups, including the CHC, local authority, District Medical Committee, Professional Advisory Committees and Staff Committees. In addition, the hope was expressed that there would be early consultation with these interests before firm plans were made.[25] The responsibility for approving plans rested initially with the management teams at each level, subsequently with the AHA and RHA, and ultimately, at some distance removed, with the DHSS.

It is important to record that while considerable emphasis was laid by the DHSS on who should be consulted, virtually no advice was given on how consultation ought to be carried out. For instance, while detailed guidance was given on topics to be covered in plans for hospital closures, none was offered on the manner of consultation.

While the DHSS may have felt that the method and scope of consultation with local bodies was a matter for local determination, it did strongly emphasise the importance of consultation in achieving both commitment and appropriate plans:

> Consultation on planning proposals is important not only as a means of securing the participation of those in the service, the community and Local Authorities with something valuable to contribute, but also for obtaining their support for the plans produced and their implementation.[26]

Indeed, a plausible interpretation of this philosophy of consultation would see it as based on a fundamental assumption (or, some might argue, misconception) that by involving all interested parties, differences of opinion on means and ends, whatever their origin, could be resolved through the planning process. At first sight, few if any of the mechanisms cited above can be said to provide for 'participation' as defined earlier in this chapter: a more accurate term would be 'consultation'. The remaining sections of this chapter therefore look at empirical evidence, to explore how much power the various groups did wield in practice, what contribution they made to policies and plans, and what effect they had on the planning process.

5 GROUP INVOLVEMENT IN NHS PLANNING: THE EXPERIENCE

As background material the authors first present, in summary form, a case study of a major planning decision taken from their research study. The chapter then considers the experience of group involvement in NHS planning in general, concentrating in particular on the expectations of the various parties, their evaluation of the costs and benefits of involvement, and the resources interest groups had available and used.

The Case Study

The planning issue discussed here is that of a change in use of a hospital from acute to geriatric care which formed part of an overall strategy designed to re-shape substantially a District's hospital facilities and concentrate its acute services in a teaching hospital. The period was the late 1970s, and the record of the episode covers a formal consultation period of three months through to the start of implementation of the changes, a further eleven months. The main bodies involved in the consultation process were the professional advisory committees; the Family Practitioner Committee (FPC); the CHC; the trade unions; a 'Save the Hospital' campaign; and the local authority. The nature and extent of their involvement is documented below.

Medical staff had been involved in the formulation of the District long-term strategy, and the approval of the appropriate medical bodies had been gained prior to the formal period of consultation on this issue. It became apparent, however, that this approval did not have the support of general practitioners at large, for the threatened hospital was much used by GPs and the teaching hospital was regarded by some of them with resentment. Their acceptance was secured by management concessions which did not affect the basic strategy. The Area Medical Advisory Committee was less involved than District-level advisory machinery until it was asked by the AHA to advise on the feasibility of counter-proposals. Its judgement against them was, at the time, given considerable weight by the AHA.

The CHC played one of the most crucial roles in this issue, by first agreeing with the change of use, and then opposing it and supporting the opposition of the local authority. Managers had from the beginning adopted the position that the CHC should be kept informed - not least because they wished to prevent the delay that would result from referral of the issue to the Secretary of State. Several meetings were held with the CHC during the consultation period, and this management approach ultimately paid off when CHC agreement to support the plan was gained in return for a number of concessions. Subsequently, however, during the latter part of the consultation period, the CHC came under much pressure from the local authority, the campaign and trade unions to change its position. This it did - after the local authority had changed most of its appointees to the CHC, those opposing the shift in attitude becoming a small minority - and subsequently acted in concert with the local authority.

The trade unions played a key role in this issue, through the medium of the Joint Shop Stewards Committee and the Trades Council, and campaigned to maintain the status quo. They felt their views were ignored by the Health Authority, appealed to the Minister to intervene (with initial success) and organised both strikes and sit-ins. The most effective pressure exerted by the unions, at least in the short run, took place after the end of the formal period of consultation, when the AHA voted to implement the change of use. The unions were able to prevent contractors entering the hospital to upgrade the wards and a stalemate resulted, for the AHA had closed the acute facilities but was unable to redevelop the hospital in any way. As this state of affairs was not to the long-term advantage of union members since it meant fewer jobs, the unions eventually capitulated, though they gained one significant policy concession from management, despite much professional opposition.

The 'Save the Hospital' campaign, of local people, trade union interests and certain hospital staff, was the most active local campaigner. Its significance lay not least in the membership of several doctors, who campaigned for the retention of the hospital as a centre for the delivery of low-technology acute, long-stay and primary care which would offer services integrated with the local community rather than isolated in a remote high-technology teaching hospital. These views influenced the demands of the campaign, trade unions, local authority and CHC, though not the bulk of the medical establishment.

This debate was continued within the Health Authority at the instigation of its local authority members. The AHA was clearly divided over the issue, but the local authority members and the one or two other members sympathetic to their cause were not able to muster a majority, not least because members with interests in other parts of the Area feared that failure to save money through rationalisation in one District would affect the development plans of other Districts.

This brief description has necessarily simplified a very complex issue. It is open to the accusation that it is a study of conflict (Lukes' 'one-dimensional view') and that it is exceptional, in that it occurred in a part of the country where community and union action was common and where shortage of resources for the health service forced major changes, threatening much-loved local institutions. Yet it was not unique[27], and for the purposes of this analysis what matters is how a planning system can stand up to the processes of group involvement, even in their most contentious form. This case study does show that the involvement of interest groups can provoke widespread conflicts over values. Managers' aims were to manage within their budget, and find a strategy acceptable locally. The CHC had great difficulty reconciling its role of representing the community with remaining on sufficiently good terms with managers to be influential. While it lacked power, it did have a formal role in planning, making it the obvious target for other groups. The prime concern of ancillary staff was job opportunities. The relevance of this issue for an analysis of the planning system is therefore that it indicates the formal consultation period will not necessarily produce consensus, and that the opposition may seek more powerful tools of influence than those provided by planning procedures. But is it possible to generalise beyond the example of a number of case studies? This can be attempted by matching the research results with various other published studies.

The Expectations of Interest Groups

What expectations did the various groups entertain during the 1970s of their involvement in health planning and policy-making? Local authorities were left by the creation of the CHC without the formal responsibility of representing local views to the NHS. Since they are conventionally seen as the local representatives of the community and, in some areas, as the local elite, this restriction of their role to merely representing the views of the organisation could be frustrating. Furthermore, as explored in the next chapter, their formal powers to influence the NHS were not very strong, making it necessary for them to seek alternative strategies if they wanted to make their views prevail.

CHCs were, throughout this period, in the position of having to establish a role for themselves distinct from, yet able to influence, a number of organisations in the health sector. This proved not to be easy. For instance, a national survey of CHCs, carried out a few years after their introduction, found that two-thirds of the CHCs in the survey had experienced some form of dispute or misunderstanding with health authorities. Two common problems were the timing of consultation (CHCs felt they should be consulted earlier in the planning process) and the effect of consultation (their seeming inability at times to have a noticeable impact upon plans).[28] Indeed, it was apparent that the objectives set for the CHC, and thus their expectations of their role, were often not matched by their ability in practice to influence decisions. This was, therefore, a source of some considerable frustration to many CHCs, who had to determine whether their long-term advantage lay in seeking maximum co-operation with management, or in attempting to remain independent.

In contrast to the efforts of CHCs, which were directed to establishing their right to be consulted, the medical profession had that right already acknowledged. Its expectation was always that its views would be followed by management; a reasonable expectation unless there were clear divisions of opinion within its own ranks. Perhaps because of this expectation, there was often little interest in participating in advisory bodies, which many doctors felt to be a tedious chore. Other professions, with the occasional exception of nurses, also seemed rarely to be much involved in planning.[29]

The degree of labour militancy varied widely over the UK in the period of the 1970s. Trade union involvement in planning issues tended to occur only in relation to specific proposals (especially hospital closures or change of use) which had implications for their members' jobs, rather than over general strategic or operational plans. On the occasions when unions were involved in planning issues, it was evident that the formal consultation process was meaningless and frustrating for them (as in the case study), not least because many managers and professionals did not accept their involvement in issues of planning strategy to be legitimate. Active union involvement was most likely to occur at the implementation stage of planning, when their expectation was to enter into 'negotiations' with management, rather than to be merely 'consulted'.

The attitude of managers towards the claims of these various groups to be involved in planning decisions was clearly a crucial factor. In general, managers appeared to accept the

need (whether as a matter of expediency or principle) to consult interested parties, while maintaining the right of the
Authority to accept or reject the views received.[30] Plans
tended to be formulated on the basis of accepted practice,
professional advice and analysis, and only later was their
acceptability to consumers, unions and local authorities considered. Plans would then be adapted only if these latter
groups could persuade managers to listen to their views. Disagreement was often ascribed by planners to a failure of the
process of communication, rather than to fundamental differences of view.

The Resources of Interest Groups

Local authorities had access to considerable human and physical resources; moreover, they possessed certain statutory
rights which provided access to health service decision-
making. However, as some studies have clearly shown, in
order to influence the NHS they had to have cards with which
to bargain, or had to attempt to build up coalitions of support, bringing together for instance CHCs, labour interests
and local authority members on the AHA (see Chapter 8). Yet
the impression throughout the 1970s was that the health service could, if it wished, plan independently of the local authority and may, indeed, have preferred such a modus vivendi.
    In contrast to local authorities, the resources of CHCs lay
primarily in their ability to become well informed about local
issues, to conduct their own (necessarily low-cost) research,
and to publicise. Their financial resources were exceedingly
modest and only supported, for the majority of CHCs, one
full-time secretary. None the less, in many Districts, CHCs
were able to undertake a very wide range of activities, were
well acquainted with 'grassroots views', and did build up considerable expertise on local health matters. Yet their lack of
information on what went on inside health authorities presented
real problems, especially in determining how best to tackle a
particular issue.
    Although CHCs possessed legitimacy in terms of their statu-
tory powers, this did not guarantee their universal acceptability to managers. Some feared or suspected that CHCs would
be influenced unduly by particular pressure groups, and would
neglect the interests of the community as a whole. Indeed,
attempting to represent the community's views, when it was
often difficult to discern a 'community', posed a considerable
problem for CHCs. The case study above revealed the very
real difficulties CHCs faced in attempting to balance the
interests of their various members and secure internal cohesiveness, especially when political activists were members
of the CHC. The role of the CHC secretary could be crucial in
this regard, both in securing credibility and providing con-
tinuity.

Predictably, perhaps, CHCs found it much easier to mobilise support over specific issues, especially at the point when local institutions were directly threatened, than over the content of general plans. This pattern of behaviour clearly implies that changes to physical entities engaged attention more readily than 'abstract' documents such as operational plans. Obviously, a CHC's capacity to be involved in planning depended much on its membership and secretary, on the time they could spare, and on their ability to select those issues where they could have an impact. Their political skills, in deciding what type of behaviour was most appropriate and in developing a network of communications and contacts, were also clearly important determinants of their ability to influence NHS managers.

These points are not unique to community involvement in the context of the NHS. It has been argued that two prerequisites exist for real community involvement.[31] First, consumers must develop a sense of group identity which will enable them to recognise the value of their particular perspective on health care issues. This may be suppressed by the low priority most consumers give to active involvement, and by the heterogeneity of interests represented in most communities. Second, consumers must develop a sense of competence in handling health care issues, though this will be hindered by the complexity of medical technology and the professional status of the physician. At best, it could be argued that the value of the CHC to the NHS was in providing a focus for the organised activity of consumers in the field of health care, backed by certain specified statutory rights, though the CHC was able to come to terms only partially with these two prerequisites.

In contrast to the experience of CHCs, professional views usually dominated, not least because of a general expectation that they should. There is little evidence that Professional Advisory Committees played a significant role, except on the infrequent occasions when Health Authorities needed to call on them for professional advice to resolve a difficult issue. Rather, issues were resolved earlier on and at lower levels. Indeed, it was apparent that the period of formal consultation could be less important than, on the one hand, the informal discussions between managers and influential professionals and advisory committees prior to the finalisation of planning proposals and, on the other, hand, the negotiations leading to implementation. In consequence, despite the existence of the NHS planning system and provision for the systematic consideration of projects, planners had difficulty combating the ability of influential clinicians to bypass the planning system and lobby decision-makers directly; and some clinicians were equally willing and able to turn the planning system to their advantage. Other tactics could include what has been termed 'shroud-waving'[32], that is indicating that the medical profession could bear no responsibility for what might happen if a particular option were to be accepted; or enlisting the media to publicise the poor fabric and equipment of particular hospitals. Such tactics tended to be used sparingly, when all other avenues of influence were exhausted.

In contrast to the real power the medical profession exercised, the power of labour interests was essentially reactive – they did not initiate proposals, but rather reacted to plans emanating from elsewhere. Their locus of power was largely local, and their influence constrained by the fragmentation of labour interests into different unions, for they necessarily found it difficult to mount a concerted opposition to health service plans, and were vulnerable to manipulation by managers. Their ultimate power lay in their ability to withdraw their labour and, when well organised, they have proved themselves well able to prevent management action, though this power was essentially negative. Moreover, although local union officials might involve themselves in issues of planning policy, the interests of their members lay primarily in employment prospects and remuneration. Only when these two areas coincided, as they did increasingly by the late 1970s, did planners need to take serious account of union views.

6 SUMMARY AND CONCLUSION

How successful has been the involvement of various groups in the NHS planning system, in terms of meeting the expectations of all parties and producing plans that took account of their views and could be implemented? The first point to make is that 'success' depends on each group's perceptions of the balance between costs and benefits. In the authors' own research work, it was evident that few of those consulted perceived much benefit to be gained from active involvement in the formal consultation process on the operational plans, or in the meetings of the Professional Advisory Committees. This view is borne out by the observations of others.[33] However, when specific proposals threatened much-loved institutions, a large number of individuals and organisations were able to mobilise in opposition, though maintaining opposition for some length of time could be very difficult.

A second point concerns the organisational characteristics, and thus the potential influence, of the groups consulted. Professional staff had considerable resources (in terms of expertise, professional skills and threat of withdrawal of co-operation); great prestige and legitimacy; a fairly high degree of organisational cohesiveness, certainly in relation to threats from outside; and political skills. Unions had few resources (except withdrawal of labour); low prestige amongst managers; and little legitimacy over planning issues. Their organisational cohesiveness was often a problem where several unions and several branches were involved. Local authorities had sizeable resources and their prestige varied, but could be considerable. They possessed a legitimate right to convey their views to the NHS, but no formal powers to prevent the health service going its own way, though influence could be exerted via the exercise of political skills. The CHCs had few resources; varying, but on the whole low prestige; some legitimacy which gave them certain limited powers over the health authority; and varying organisational cohesiveness and political skills.

A third point concerns the ease with which interested parties could follow the mechanics of the planning system. NHS plans were frequently complex and lengthy, and those consulted often felt that inadequate data to justify proposals were provided to them. Moreover, consultation was usually based on a firm proposal which managers had already decided was the best option. This explains the increasing concern of CHCs and local authorities to be involved early in the planning process. However, such early involvement, even when it materialised, did not ensure that their views were followed, and officers and members were anxious to emphasise that requesting views did not commit them to follow them. Indeed, the many pressures on managers, from higher tiers and from local dominant interests, could limit considerably their ability to satisfy conflicting demands from other quarters.

It is now possible to return to the definitions of participation, consultation and negotiation presented in section 2, and to explore the implications of group involvement for the planning and policy-making process. First, where interested parties such as CHCs, trade unions and local authorities expected to 'participate' and have an impact on plans, the 'consultation' process could prove . unsatisfactory and frustrating. It is, however, fair to add that not all groups had this expectation, but were satisfied with the opportunity to express their views; and on issues which did not arouse basic conflicts of interest, the consultation process could prove satisfying to all parties concerned. Second, there was little evidence that the consultation process, and the setting up of CHCs, had led to any significant change in the balance of power. None the less, managers learnt that it was to their advantage to keep the CHC informed. Third, opposition to plans might not become fully evident, or indeed be stimulated, until the stage when plans were implemented; and apparent agreement during formal consultation might not persist through implementation. Finally, managers needed to be prepared, and able to cope, when a consultation process was turned into a negotiating process through the exercise of power by an interested party. A common attitude of managers was that CHCs and unions did not have the 'right' to negotiate. This attitude could hamper the management of conflict, and produce protracted disputes when quicker resolution of the issues might have been possible.

What lessons can be learnt from the experience of the NHS which might be transferable to other countries and other health sectors? The first is concerned with the value of providing a forum, such as the CHC, to voice consumer interests. In England, CHCs have provided those least able with an opportunity to assert their own interests. Moreover, despite all their limitations as a source of major influence on policy and decision-making, they have gone some way towards demonstrating that, as formally constituted bodies, they can function as a focal point for the generation of a 'consumer' view on health service issues. For similar reasons, it might be considered important to have a forum at a local level for the expression and reconciliation of conflicting views about priorities. The significance of the Health Authority was that it provided a mechanism, albeit imperfect, whereby the various interests of clinicians, local authority councillors, CHCs, trade unions and managers could be resolved via debate and negotiation and, if ultimately necessary, settled by a vote.

The next is that, once it is agreed that there are definite advantages in the involvement of various groups in health planning and policy-making, a planning system can provide a ready opportunity for the articulation of views. While this does not necessarily prevent greater weight being given to particular interests, a published plan can bring the debate into the open, and force each group to justify its stance publicly. Any country also has to give careful consideration to who should be involved, and whether this involvement should take the form of, for instance, consultation or participation.

Whatever the level and form of involvement, it is highly likely that it will provoke some degree of conflict and disagreement. Individuals or organisations that do not achieve what they seek are likely to feel that their involvement was ineffective, no matter how well information was provided or views sought, or how much time was devoted to discussions. It is most important, therefore, if they are to continue to involve themselves, that they feel they have had a fair hearing. In the NHS, community and staff involvement in planning was introduced at a peculiarly difficult time when the traditional expectation that resources for the NHS would always increase was overturned. Lack of money has highlighted issues of priorities and values. The resulting conflicts have showed up in the participative and consultative processes and indicated, perhaps more clearly than ever before, the importance of viewing planning as a political as much as a technical process.

NOTES

1. S. R. Arnstein, A Ladder of Citizen Participation,

'American Institute of Planners Journal' (July 1969), pp. 216-24.

2. C. J. Ham, Community Health Council Participation in the NHS Planning System, 'Social Policy and Administration', vol. 14, no. 3 (Autumn 1980).

3. S. Lukes, 'Power, a Radical View' (Macmillan, London, 1974).

4. P. Bachrach and M. S. Baratz, The Two Faces of Power, 'American Political Science Review', vol. 56 (1972), pp. 947-52.

5. M. Fagence, 'Citizen Participation in Planning' (Pergamon Press, Oxford, 1977).

6. C. Pateman, 'Participation and Democratic Theory' (Cambridge University Press, Cambridge, 1970).

7. P. Marris and M. Rein, 'Dilemmas of Social Reform' (Routledge and Kegan Paul, London, 1967).

8. M. Emery (ed.), 'Searching for New Directions, in New Ways, for New Times', Occasional Papers in Continuing Education, no. 12 (Centre for Continuing Education, Australian National University, Canberra, 1976).

9. Skeffington Report, 'People and Planning' (HMSO, London, 1969).

10. Ham, Community Health Council Participation, p. 224.

11. See, for instance, P. Levin, Opening Up the Planning Process in S. Hatch (ed.), 'Towards Participation in Local Services', Fabian Tract 419 (1973), on the effect of planning procedures; and Skeffington, 'People and Planning', on the importance of planners' attitudes.

12. J. G. Davies, 'The Evangelistic Bureaucrat: a Study of a Planning Exercise in Newcastle-upon-Tyne' (Tavistock Publications, London, 1972).

13. H. Eckstein, 'Pressure Group Politics' (Allen and Unwin, London, 1960).

14. R. Taylor, The Local Health System: an Ethnography of Interest Groups and Decision-Making, 'Social Science and Medicine', no. 11 (1977), pp. 593-98.

15. S. Cang, Community Health Councils: Intentions, Problems and Possibilities in E. Jacques (ed.), 'Health Services: their Nature and Organisation, and the Role of Patients, Doctors and the Health Professions' (Brunel Health Services Organisation Research Unit, 1978).

16. DHSS, 'Community Health Councils', HRC(74)4 (1974).

17. R. Klein and J. Lewis, 'The Politics of Consumer Representation' (Centre for Studies in Social Policy, 1976).

18. DHSS, 'The National Health Service (Community Health Councils) Regulations', 1973, SI(73)2217 (1974).

19. DHSS, 'Health Services Management: Report of Working Party on Devolution', HC(76)37 (1976).

20. See, for instance, J. Hallas, 'Mounting the Health Guard' (Nuffield Provincial Hospitals Trust, London, 1974); and

D. Phillips, The Creation of Consultative Councils in the NHS, 'Public Administration', vol. 58 (Spring 1980).

21. DHSS, 'Management Arrangements for the Reorganised NHS' (HMSO, London, 1972).

22. See, for instance, S. Haywood and A. Alaszewski, 'Crisis in the Health Service: the Politics of Management' (Croom Helm, London, 1980).

23. DHSS, 'Participative Management', HC(76)44 (1976).

24. S. J. Dimmock, Participation or Control? The Workers' Involvement in Management in K. Barnard and K. Lee (eds.), 'Conflicts in the NHS' (Croom Helm, London, 1977).

25. DHSS, 'The NHS Planning System' (HMSO, London, 1976), p. 22.

26. Ibid., p. 6.

27. Mersey Regional Health Authority, 'Report of the Liverpool Committee of Inquiry' (January 1978).

28. A. Dunford, 'Planning for the Consumer: the Views of Community Health Councils' (Essex University, mimeo., 1977).

29. See, for instance, Royal Commission on the National Health Service, 'The Working of the NHS', Research Paper No. 1 (HMSO, London, 1978), pp. 62-6.

30. Ibid., pp. 92-3.

31. E. P. Stoller, New Roles for Health Care Consumers: a Study of Role Transformation, 'Journal of Community Health', vol. 3, no. 2 (Winter 1977).

32. R. Taylor, The Local Health System: Observations on the Exercise of Professional Influence, 'Health and Social Service Journal', Centre Eight Papers (1977).

33. R. G. S. Brown, 'The Management of Welfare' (Fontana/Collins, London, 1975).

1 THE NEED FOR LINKAGES

Conventional wisdom now recognises that the state of health of a community is the result of the complex interaction of many factors. As a consequence, if a government wishes to promote health, it must take account of the health impact of a wide range of different activities and policies. These activities, for reasons explored later, will be the responsibility of a large number of different organisations, many of them outside the health sector. There is therefore a need, now widely acknowledged, to promote 'linkages' between organisations, to co-ordinate policies and activities.

Such liaison between organisations goes under a variety of names (such as 'inter-organisational relationships' and 'networking') and can be classified by its purpose into three main types. First, it is argued that there is a need to promote linkages to ensure that a variety of organisations, both public and private, consider the impact that their policies and activities have on the health of the population. This concern is demonstrated by the World Health Organization (WHO) in its promotion of Primary Health Care:

Health cannot be attained by the health sector alone. In developing countries in particular, economic development, anti-poverty measures, food production, water, sanitation, housing, environmental protection and education all contribute to health and have the same goal of human development. Primary health care, as an integral part of the health system and of overall social and economic development, will of necessity rest on proper co-ordination at all levels between the health and all other sectors concerned.[1]

This argument is a general one that applies also to developed countries, though formulated in terms of different diseases and different disease determinants. For instance, in England the need for co-ordination was recognised by the Royal Commission on the National Health Service, which stated that the achievement of a prime objective of the NHS, to encourage and assist individuals to remain healthy, demanded co-operation particularly with housing, planning and environmental health departments, and with industry; and further, that the

147

promotion of health required co-operation with such bodies as education departments, sport and leisure organisations, commerce and the food and drinks industry.[2] The report in 1980 of the DHSS working party on inequalities in health [3] provided further evidence of the need to co-ordinate a great variety of organisations if health improvements were to be achieved. This report showed that, despite the availability of health services irrespective of ability to pay since 1948, marked differences in mortality and morbidity rates between social classes persisted and could be attributed to a broad range of factors including the socio-economic environment (for instance work accidents, overcrowding, smoking), the availability and accessibility of high-quality health services, and the more diffuse consequences of the class structure, including poverty and deprivation amongst certain groups.

Second, linkages are considered necessary between organisations providing related services, on the grounds that these should be planned, developed and run in order to make the most effective use of resources. In England, health services (such as health centres and hospitals) and social services (such as hostels, residential care and community support) are provided by different organisations. Yet in a number of instances, the services they provide are closely connected (long-stay geriatric wards and old people's homes, for example), the operation of one service is affected by decisions taken by the other service, and the services have some clients in common. Similar arguments for linkages between related services can be made with respect to, for example, medical services and the traditional health sector in both developing and developed countries.

Third, it can be argued that linkages are necessary between the various organisations providing health care. This is an issue even in those countries (such as England) where the great majority of health services come under one broad organisational umbrella, for such an arrangement does not necessarily ensure co-ordination between sub-units. Co-ordination can be considered even more vital in countries such as the US or Third World countries such as Brazil, Mexico and Thailand, where the formal health system is fragmented, services being provided by a variety of different government, para-statal, voluntary and private organisations.

What types of activities might these linkages co-ordinate? They may include:

(1)   day-to-day collaboration over individual patients or clients;
(2)   operational management issues; or
(3)   long-term policy-making and planning, concerned with setting priorities and with major resource allocation decisions.

Interest in the topic of linkages between organisations has resulted not only from an acknowledgement of the need to consider all influences on health, but also from recognition that, whatever the theoretical arguments, organisations providing health-related services tend in practice to operate in isolation from each other. Staff in different organisations often have no clear motive to co-operate, and while organisations may be dependent on others to help them achieve their goals, each organisation has its own set of loyalties, legal responsibilities, values and professional affiliations that are likely to hamper co-ordination and co-operation.

In consequence, a range of possible outcomes, involving different degrees of co-operation, can be distinguished[4]:

(1)   unconnected planning, where each organisation plans without reference to others;

(2)   independent planning based on shared information, where each organisation is aware of the others' plans, but otherwise plans on its own;

(3)   joint bargaining, where organisations, despite different goals and priorities, recognise they can gain mutual benefit from negotiations about future plans; and

(4)   joint planning based on shared goals, where organisations work together from the earliest stages of planning through to plan implementation.

These four possible outcomes lie behind much of the debate about what type of co-ordination is desirable and what, in the face of organisational realities, is feasible. The first part of this chapter discusses the theoretical aspects of this debate. This is followed by an analysis of the co-ordination of health and related services in Britain, which attempts to identify the potential for developing health policy and planning linkages between organisations and the constraints which such developments face.

2 PATTERNS OF GOVERNMENT ORGANISATION

What factors might influence government organisation, and determine how functions are allocated, co-ordinated and performed? Why are various responsibilities and functions split between different organisations? In discussing this issue, it is helpful to refer to four 'competing' principles which may shape organisational patterns.[5] In brief, the 'areal' principle is reflected in the constitutional or legal arrangements for the division (or delegation) of powers between central and local government. The 'client' principle suggests that each organisation should be more or less exclusively responsible for a defined sub-group of the population. The 'process' principle refers to the advantages of concentrating specialised skills and techniques within the same organisation. However, in theory at least, it is the fourth principle of organisation, the 'purpose' served, which is the guiding force in determining the pattern of most organisations of government.

The division of responsibilities, and hence of activities, between departments or organisations will depend also on the character of the administrative system. Here it is helpful to make a distinction between a 'pluralist' and a 'unitary' system. In a pluralist system, there is a proliferation of separate agencies both 'horizontally' at the same level of government and 'vertically' at regional and local level, and each agency will have a considerable degree of autonomy. In a unitary system, the multiplication of agencies is limited and their powers and mutual relationships carefully regulated.

These institutional patterns reflect different political theories of government.[6] Political pluralism views society as composed of competing groups and interests, and considers that the administrative system does or should reflect these social demands. Various agencies will be created to respond to the demands of various social groups and, therefore, a multiplicity of agencies will indicate an appropriate response to differing social needs. Acceptance of this pluralist view of government implies acceptance of administrative duplication, since the needs of clients overlap, and of administrative conflict since this parallels, to some extent, the conflicts between social groups. Failures of administrative co-ordination can, in this view, be seen as the price to be paid for strengthening the effectiveness of agencies in reaching their (separate) goals.[7]

A contrasting view is provided by a theory of democracy rooted in unitary principles. This view is prevalent as an ideal in Britain, for instance, where it is expected that political parties and leaders should synthesise the demands of social groups, and produce a coherent and consistent programme capable of being implemented through the administrative system. A change of political leadership may cause agency policies to change, but administrative conflict is seen as undesirable. In consequence, co-ordination between organisations is more likely to emerge as a concern in a unitary than in a pluralist system.

Indeed, in England, government interest in co-ordination reflects both a unitary perspective and a response to existing patterns of organisation. The NHS is expected to 'collaborate' with a number of local authority departments for many (unitary) reasons: in most cases they serve the same population (areal principle); in some cases they provide different services to the same client group; in others, the processes or skills involved in providing different services are very similar and there are seen to be good grounds for sharing scarce skills; and in yet other instances, there is considered to be a congruence of purpose. The question this poses is whether the emphasis placed on these various aspects (commonality of purpose, area, clients or process) results in different patterns of linkage and influences their effectiveness.

It is certainly likely that the rationale for linkages will influence considerably the degree to which members of organisations perceive linkages to be to their advantage. However, using the terms defined in the previous chapter, will linkages take the form of collaboration, that is of joint planning based on shared goals, or merely of consultation or even of negotiation? Anticipating what type of linkage is likely to occur, formulating recommendations on how linkages can best be encouraged, and determining what structures and processes are most useful, depend on taking a view of what factors influence organisational behaviour. This issue is explored further in the next section.

3 THEORETICAL APPROACHES TO ORGANISATIONAL LINKAGES

In the UK, theoretical discussions of organisational linkages have taken place largely within the context of land-use planning and public administration. Four distinct theoretical approaches can be identified[8], in part representing the historical evolution of ideas in Britain and the US, but each reflecting a different theoretical perspective, and thus leading to different normative models.

The first approach depends essentially on a unitary perspective. Co-ordination results from central direction, often through a central plan which specifies goals, programmes and targets for the various government departments and sectors. Since, in its purest form, this approach is over-rigid and impracticable, a less centralised system is adopted in practice, though still conforming to what was termed, in Chapter 3, the 'rational comprehensive' model. In this approach, it is assumed not only that different organisations will come to perceive that co-operation is both in their interest and in the interests of their clients, but also that a consensus will emerge on future developments. As Chapter 3 discussed in detail, this approach can be criticised for assuming that organisations will want to agree and clarify mutual goals for, in practice, they may see themselves in a conflict or bargaining situation, and be concerned to pursue their own interests.

The second approach argues that linkages are not promoted by formal arrangements, but rather by allowing each organisation to act independently, anticipating and adjusting as far as possible to the actions of others.[9] In this context, linkages cannot be promoted by co-ordinating structures unless co-operation is perceived to be in the organisations' mutual interests; in short, partisan mutual adjustment takes place.

This view thus favours a pluralist model of society operating on laissez-faire principles.

More recently, a third approach has emerged, drawing both on the incrementalism of the second approach and on ideas on appropriate organisational behaviour in a 'turbulent' environment. Friend and his collaborators have been responsible for major contributions to this approach.[10] They view organisations as interacting responsively with their environment, and concerned to develop linkages where mutual benefit can be obtained. To assist this process, the idea of a decision network, which links people interested in the same type of decisions in different organisations, has been developed. The network may include formal structures, but is essentially informal, incorporating actors whose concern is to develop new approaches to coping with a rapidly changing environment, to increase organisational effectiveness. Particular stress is placed on the flow of information between organisations, and on the need to develop the linking skills of the network members.

These ideas were further developed, in the context of inter-agency committees, by Noad and King,[11] who list various characteristics, both internal to the committees and external, involving the relationship of committee members to their parent bodies, which hamper co-ordination and joint working. Among the internal characteristics listed are:

(1) different terminologies, methods of working and theories held by professional groups, often resulting in rivalry;

(2) lack of understanding of the roles of different individuals and the interests they represent, particularly among officers and elected members;

(3) competition for resources and control among departments and organisations in order to increase their relative power;

(4) ritualistic structures for the participation of various interests;

(5) unreasonable expectations about the ability of others to effect changes; and

(6) lack of understanding of the internal operations and cultures of other organisations.

Those characteristics, from the perspective of the wider external system, which might damage the chances of linkages developing are:

(1) poor support for joint approaches from central policy-makers, and a lack of commitment by parent departments;

(2) lack of input from joint activities to corporate decision processes, such as budgeting and planning cycles;

(3) bureaucratic subversion of agreed decisions; and
(4) isolation of co-ordinating structures due to weak communication channels.

The fourth and final approach considered here has been developed by writers who wished to consider organisational linkages primarily in terms of power and control over resources.[12] Benson, for example, argues that some organisations are more powerful than others because they directly command more resources and/or they are connected to dominant interest groups in the wider social structure.[13] These organisations will have an enhanced bargaining power in any network. Thus indulging in network activities may not be done with the objective of achieving mutual benefit (as Friend suggests), but rather of manipulating other organisations, and increasing resources. Conversely, a lack of co-ordination may not be the result of poor communication of each organisation's problems and interests, but rather the result of conflicts of interest that cannot be resolved through improved communication or better bargaining. If the latter is true, then the organisation may fall back on Lindblom's partisan mutual adjustment.

This argument can be extended. Each organisation is likely to contain competing and conflicting interest groups, and attempts at organisational linkages may threaten the relative status and influence of various occupational groups. Thus an organisation may be divided within itself on the potential benefit to be gained from co-ordination. Moreover, it can be plausibly argued that such benefits are less likely to be realised when the financial resources available to each organisation are declining.[14] For instance, organisations may wish to lighten their work-load and avoid new commitments, thus restricting the scope for negotiation.

Each of these four approaches to organisational linkages – the rational comprehensive approach, the incrementalist approach, the decision network approach and the political economy approach – embodies a different theoretical model of the way organisations behave, posing the question of which most nearly approximates to reality. The significance of this question lies in its relevance to any attempt to prescribe effective mechanisms for linkages. The next sections therefore examine this issue in the context of a case study of organisational linkages in the health sector in England.

4 LOCAL LINKAGES IN THE ENGLISH NHS

Introduction: the Rationale

Many commentators heralded the 1970s as a new era in social policy determination when, for probably the first time, attention was paid nationally to the totality of social policy, with an emphasis on co-ordinating the attack on social problems, in particular poverty.[15] A review of government co-ordination mechanisms for social policies argued: 'There is a need to consider together all policies which are concerned with the distribution of resources and opportunities among the community, and with ways of changing that distribution.'[16] As a result of that review (known as 'A Joint Approach to Social Policies' or JASP), a new social policy group of senior Ministers was established, to take a forward look at policies in the light of demographic, distributional and other factors. In addition, a number of inter-departmental studies were set up.[17] Whilst it was no doubt anticipated that barriers to JASP existed, such as Ministerial independence [18] and traditional departmental working practices[19], the architects of JASP hoped that these national attempts at co-ordination would bring into the open the disagreements about policy that stemmed from the different priorities and concerns of departments, and facilitate their resolution.

At the same time, JASP at the national level was being matched by various local experiments in joint policy-making in the form, for instance, of comprehensive community programmes and inner-city partnerships.[20] However, health formed one element only of these experiments, and rather a minor one, and they were confined to a few geographical locations. In contrast, a nation-wide policy of co-ordination, focused on health and therefore of particular interest in this book, developed from the consideration given, from 1971 onwards, to how best 'collaboration' between the NHS and local government could be achieved. The objective of such collaboration was set out clearly in the following way:

> The purpose of the re-organisation of the NHS is to enable services to the patient to be improved. But the health services cannot be operated or developed in isolation: they depend on the humane planning and provision of a range of closely related services which are the responsibility of local government. It is therefore of great importance for the new health authorities to forge effective links and foster close understanding with their counterparts, the local authorities responsible for personal social services, education, housing, and public health.[21]

Subsequently, in relation to the nature and extent of planning linkages between the two authorities, the policy was laid down that:

> NHS planning must, therefore, take into account and integrate with Local Authority plans for personal social services, environmental health, housing, education, and transport. The aim is for coherent and comprehensive

planning on a wide front, to produce effective joint plans for interdependent services.[22]

The rationale for local joint approaches was that in general they would enable authorities to:

(1) switch resources to where the need was perceived to be greatest – including areas of need which crossed the boundaries between the responsibilities of different agencies or departments;

(2) choose together the most effective ways of achieving a given end;

(3) ensure that in cases where one form of provision could not proceed without services run by another agency, both were provided;

(4) avoid situations in which one policy, service or agency hampered another (such as creation or aggravation of health problems by insensitive local government planning);

(5) provide resources from more than one policy area, service or agency where one of these alone could not produce the full potential benefits;

(6) achieve economies of scale through sharing facilities.[23]

Linkage Mechanisms

The kind of thinking outlined above was reflected closely in the structures and processes established to facilitate linkages between the NHS and local government from 1974 onwards. In detail, the NHS Reorganisation Act (1973) stipulated that Areas should normally be coterminous with counties, and laid a general duty on Area Health Authorities to collaborate with local authorities. One NHS tier thus had a clear responsibility for collaboration. Under the same Act, Joint Consultative Committees (JCCs) of members from AHAs, County and District Councils were established to advise constituent health and local authorities on the planning and operation of services of common concern. Further, each Area Health Authority and its matching local authority was asked to establish a Joint Care Planning Team (JCPT) of officers to advise on the development of strategic plans and guidelines for key services identified by the JCC. Indeed, in the new management structure of the NHS, certain posts carried special responsibility for developing linkages and joint plans. Finally, from 1976/7, the Secretary of State made available to health authorities special earmarked finance, 'joint finance' as it was called, to allocate to selected projects for which local authorities bore the prime responsibility and which made a contribution to total care.

These structural features and mechanisms were intended to encourage the health service to plan services jointly with local authorities, in particular with their social services departments. The fact that the raison d'être of one tier was collaboration, that there were specific posts with a major responsibility for joint planning, that there was a statutory requirement to set up JCCs, and that government guidance existed on JCPTs, meant that at the very least forums existed within which collaboration and joint planning could be discussed. Furthermore, joint finance was introduced as a strong financial incentive to promote linkages. How have these mechanisms worked in practice?

The Operation of Planning Linkages

For the purpose of analysis, each of the above structural features and mechanisms is considered in turn.

Coterminosity. Considerable emphasis was placed, in the early 1970s, on the desirability of common geographical boundaries for health and local authorities. Indeed, this principle was an important rationale for the creation of an Area tier, coterminous with County Councils (except in London, which had a different local government structure). Different commentators have taken up very different stances on the merits of this principle: some argue that collaboration does not demand coterminosity[24]; others that coterminosity is helpful and collaboration would be more difficult to develop in its absence.[25]

The authors' research in an urban area of London where coterminosity existed at District level and, hence, where the AHA had to link with a number of local authorities, indicated that coterminosity made collaboration over planning issues potentially much easier at District level than at Area level, where the large number of collaborating authorities greatly hampered discussions and increased their complexity and potential for conflict. In another area with a more conventional structure, coterminosity between the AHA and County Council assisted strategic planning, though co-ordination between the County Council and Health Districts on operational policies and plans was more difficult to develop.[26] In summary, coterminosity can facilitate but by no means guarantee collaboration, for co-ordination is inevitably complex between two multi-tiered organisations, each with responsibilities divided between tiers, and different concepts of what ought to be the appropriate organisational size for its various functions. In 1974, emphasis on the AHA level reflected the stress placed at that time on links with the County Council. New proposals in 1980 for reorganising the NHS structure do not attach the same importance to the principle of coterminosity.[27]

Joint Consultative Committee. The JCC, as a committee of part-elected, part-appointed members with no formal powers, depended vitally on the interest, personalities and influence of its members. As such, they could provide a focus for the work of the officers, inject a sense of urgency, and have some form of legitimating function. On the other hand, they have been frequently criticised for acting as mere 'rubber stamps' and for lacking initiative. Predictably, the role of the JCC has been heavily dependent on the relationship of officers to members in each organisation. Moreover, on issues of vital importance, the parent authorities have on occasion perceived their advantage to lie in negotiating directly with each other, rather than via a co-ordinating body such as the JCC, and through officer level negotiation, rather than through members.

Joint Care Planning Team. Since 1976, the JCPT has been the body which, at Area level, has been given prime responsibility for developing joint planning and, hence, possessed the potential for identifying trade-offs and agreements. However, two major problems have emerged in its operation. First, rather than developing the joint policies, based on common goals, that the DHSS intended it should, officers have often been more concerned to attempt to influence the other organisation in ways that suited the interests of their own organisation. For example, in one area studied each authority tended to view the process of joint planning primarily as a means of helping to resolve some of the pressures and deficiencies in their own services.[28] Moreover, NHS officers often perceived the areas of interest common to both organisations to be fairly peripheral to the prime concerns of the NHS.

Second, the JCPT, located at Area level, could not closely concern itself with operational issues, since these were a District responsibility. It thus tended to concentrate on strategic planning issues. But strategic issues often lacked urgency, and thus there could be little pressure to make progress; and local authority interests often lay primarily in the operation of services, especially when a local authority did not operate a forward planning system. The introduction of joint finance did concentrate the attention of JCPTs on specific services, but these were often planned by the local authority in isolation from the NHS. In consequence, collaboration tended to be seen in very narrow terms, concerned with the social services on which joint finance could be spent rather than with the wider determinants of health status.

Joint Finance. The DHSS heralded joint financing as an innovation which would allow field authorities greater flexibility in making decisions on the balance of care within their communities. Where a need for a social service that would assist the work of the NHS was identified, the health authority could make joint finance money available for the project to the local authority if it was reluctant or unable to fund the project itself. As joint financing was introduced at the same time that the joint planning arrangements came into effect, it has generally been regarded both as an incentive to encourage authorities to make use of the machinery for collaboration, and as an indirect means for the DHSS to channel money to social services departments in order to facilitate a shift of emphasis away from hospital care towards community care. There are two important questions to be asked: how far has joint financing permitted greater flexibility in local decision-making, and how far has it acted as an incentive to authorities to undertake joint planning?

On the first point, the degree of flexibility was itself constrained by the conditions attached to the use of joint finance, although these have been relaxed somewhat over time. Originally, it was anticipated that the majority would be spent on capital expenditure, with any revenue support diminishing over five years, and the local authority gradually assuming full responsibility. While some local authorities took up their quota of joint finance others, particularly in the more rural and fiscally conservative parts of the country, were more hesitant. Their concern was that with any continuing scheme, the local authority had to meet the costs of running that scheme once the joint finance support was phased out.[29]

So to what extent has joint financing acted as an incentive to joint planning? Not surprisingly, there has been some resentment amongst NHS managers that they have been obliged to spend money on local authority services rather than on NHS services which they considered deserved higher priority. Likewise, some local authorities have resented or resisted putting their high-priority schemes at risk, in order to pick up the revenue consequences of perhaps less important schemes implemented because they were eligible for joint funding. As was intended, joint finance has made each agency at least to some extent adjust to the priorities of the other. Evidence does also exist that joint finance saved projects that would have been abandoned through lack of money; encouraged schemes that have benefited directly client groups long neglected by the health service[30]; gave teeth to the collaboration machinery; and provided staff from the two organisations with a specific purpose to meet and thus to get to know each other's points of view.

Consultation Procedures. In addition to these collaborative activities, local authorities were entitled to be consulted on Area plans. This topic was investigated in Chapter 7, and to reiterate its conclusion, where an organisation (local authority or NHS) feels a vital interest is at stake, it will want to be more than just consulted. Yet there are areas of concern, especially affecting professional practices, where an organisation will not recognise the right of other organisations to do more than state their views. Thus, over issues where the NHS feels its interests are threatened, it may construe its task to be merely to consult the local authority, rather than to collaborate.

5   LESSONS FOR THE UK

DHSS recommendations and guidelines on collaboration have been couched in the language of rational analysis, and from a unitary perspective, but is this an appropriate perspective to apply to the NHS? In terms of the various outcomes of collaboration identified in section 1, it would appear that there has been some unconnected planning; some independent planning, based on shared information gained through the JCPT, JCC and the consultative processes; some joint bargaining, especially over joint finance; and very little joint planning. Why this might be so is considered below in terms of the characteristics (listed earlier) that Noad and King suggest may constrain the successful operation of co-ordinating structures.

External Influences

Noad and King argue that the success of joint planning will be influenced both by the support from central policy-makers and by the degree of commitment of field authorities. Throughout the 1970s, there clearly was central government support for collaboration between health authorities and local authorities (especially their social services departments). Furthermore, joint finance was introduced as an incentive to bring health and local authorities closer together. However, DHSS policies are mediated by several levels of management, whose primary concern may be to maintain traditionally defined 'health' services. Certainly, this was the view of many social service officials, who found themselves collaborating with medicine's so-called 'cinderella' specialties: 'In the NHS, the highest status and priority still goes to the acute specialties while psychiatry and geriatrics, where co-operation with social services agencies counts, remain minor concerns.'[31] It follows that, in future, local authority personnel may be more strongly motivated and experience less frustration if they perceive that their area of common concern with the NHS is more highly ranked by its officers.

Noad and King also argue that the success of joint arrangements is likely to be related to the extent to which schemes conceived jointly are adopted by parent agencies. On the whole, mechanisms did exist to link JCC and JCPT decisions to each authority's planning and budgeting system. However, the structure of each organisation materially affected the operation of the co-ordinating bodies and impeded their attempts to introduce change. The AHA was part of a much larger NHS corporate structure and the social services department, the other party most affected, was securely tied to the wider political and organisational structure of the local authority. Thus, even if both the local authority and higher tiers of the NHS were sympathetic to the principle of collaboration, in practice their actions on occasion imposed unpopular policies on their respective local agencies which damaged collaboration, but which the local agencies were not free to alter.

Internal Influences

Turning to the internal characteristics of co-ordinating committees, and again following Noad and King's approach, the problem of different terminologies, methods of working and theories held by professional groups appeared to be less of a problem at the management level concerned primarily with strategic planning and policy-making than at an operational level. However, there was a clear difference between the relative roles of officers and members in each organisation. Health authority members tended to have little influence, and were accustomed to rely heavily on officer guidance. In contrast, local authority members were used to a more influential relationship with their own officers, and some felt resentment and frustration at what they considered to be the cavalier fashion in which their comments on health service issues were treated. In short, elected members of local authorities expected to be the decision-makers, whereas traditionally the role of the non-elected NHS members had largely been confined to validating officer decisions.

Relations should improve in the future as staff in the two organisations become accustomed to each other's way of working. In the early days, participants were still very aware of their individual identities as representatives of particular organisations, and the meetings both of officer groups (JCPTs) and of members (JCCs) tended to be formal and often ritualistic. Immediate issues, and particularly important issues, tended to be handled outside the formal machinery. Thus:

In spite of expressions of goodwill and good personal relations the joint committees themselves were fairly peripheral for the first two or three years . . . Points raised at AHA meetings were referred to the consultative committees, but not much came back. Other commitments kept committee meetings short and not well attended.[32]

Many of these internal issues stem from lack of knowledge and experience, which can fairly easily be remedied, if the interest to do so exists. Indeed, one of the most significant features of collaboration experience so far, one which has been noted also by other commentators[33], is that the incentive to collaborate is closely bound up with the major problems facing the organisation, and with command over resources. Noad and King mention that competition for resources and for control among departments and organisations can be a disruptive influence within co-ordinating committees. Yet it may be basic to their involvement, as suggested by the impact of joint finance on the relationship of health and local authorities. It is also clear, however, that different organisational structures, management patterns and planning systems do constitute a significant barrier, even when good intentions exist or when potential benefits for the organisation exist from linkages. In other words, co-ordinating structures can at best provide a framework for collaboration, but they do not guarantee it.

6   CONCLUSION

What are the conclusions that can be drawn from the experience of the UK? In some respects, there have been more contacts between the NHS and local authorities than cynics might have expected; in other respects the practice has not approached the DHSS ideal.[34] Yet there are some lessons to be drawn from the emerging practice that are helpful in devising appropriate strategies for linkages within the health sector and with related sectors.

First, those designing linking structures and procedures should not assume that a consensus on goals is necessarily feasible. In particular, health-specific agencies should not assume that the achievement of health for all is necessarily a goal common to all health-related agencies - it may be so at a philosophical level, but is unlikely to influence the daily activities of an organisation. Instead, organisations should identify specific areas for linkages, where greatest potential exists. These are likely to be in areas where organisations need each other's resources and skills; where the services of linking organisations are complementary; and where common interests exist. Such circumstances provide a basis for negotiation, concession and compromise as long as each organisation holds something of value to the other organisation, and is capable of resisting its demands. In other words, the balance of power between the organisations must be appropriate.

Second, such negotiations are likely to be easier to develop and conclude over operational issues which have a more immediate significance than over strategic planning issues. Moreover, any agreements reached over strategic issues run the danger of disguising basic differences of approach which become apparent only at the implementation stage, and require the issue to be re-negotiated.

Third, an organisation, if it has a sufficiently dominant

position, may be able to lay down the nature of the linkages to be established by subordinate agencies. It is more likely, however, that such an authoritarian strategy will not be productive. In such a case, linkages may best be promoted if the local agency has some discretion and freedom of manoeuvre to establish linkages where locally appropriate. Such a process may be assisted where political support for co-ordination can be mobilised in the community or nationally.

Fourth, the use of financial incentives to encourage appropriate linkages can be of great assistance; conversely, those linkages may be made more difficult to promote when resources are very scarce, or when one agency threatens the resources of another, for instance by diverting funds away from it or by encroaching on its area of responsibility.

Fifth, given the strength of the vested interests of professionals in any sector, the potential for linkages will be greatest where professional perspectives are not over-dominant, and where the likelihood of rivalries and disagreements between professions is minimised.

To conclude, links between organisations providing health-related services are not necessarily promoted by assuming that a consensus exists on goals and activities. Rather, policy-makers should identify those areas which have the greatest potential for setting up linkages; should identify the likely internal and external constraints that might damage such linkages; and then look for effective collaborative strategies, including the introduction of incentives. Both formal and informal processes of linkage will be necessary. Structural arrangements cannot, by themselves, guarantee linkages, but they do provide forums for discussion. None the less, informal processes, organised by people with planning and liaison roles and possessing understanding and commitment, may prove to be the most fruitful way of securing effective linkages.

NOTES

1. WHO, 'Primary Health Care', a Joint Report by the Director-General of WHO and the Executive Director of UNICEF (Geneva/New York, 1978).
2. K. Richards, 'The NHS and Social Services', King's Fund Project Paper No. RC11 (1980).
3. DHSS, 'Inequalities in Health', Report of a Research Working Group (under the Chairmanship of Sir Douglas Black) (HMSO, London, 1980).
4. D. Towell, 'Approaches to Joint Care Planning' (Nuffield Centre for Health Services Studies, mimeo., Leeds, 1977).
5. P. Self, 'Administrative Theories and Politics' (Allen and Unwin, London, 1974), Chapter Two.
6. Ibid., pp. 87-9.
7. D. Braybrooke and C. E. Lindblom, 'A Strategy of

Decision' (Free Press, New York, 1963).
8. P. Healey, Networking as a Normative Principle, with Particular Reference to Local Government and Land Use Planning, 'Local Government Studies', vol. 5, no. 1 (1979), pp. 55-68.
9. C. E. Lindblom, 'The Limits to Democracy' (Free Press, New York, 1964).
10. J. K. Friend and W. N. Jessop, 'Local Government and Strategic Choice: an Operational Research Approach to the Processes of Public Planning' (Pergamon, Oxford, 1967); and J. K. Friend, J. M. Power and C. J. L. Yewlett, 'Public Planning: the Inter-Corporate Dimension' (Tavistock Publications, London, 1974).
11. A. Noad and L. King, Area Co-ordination: Some Experiences Compared, 'Linkage Two' (1977).
12. Healey, Networking as a Normative Principle, pp. 59-61.
13. J. K. Benson, The Interorganisational Network as a Political Economy, 'Administrative Science Quarterly', vol. 20 (1975).
14. H. Glennerster, From Containment to Conflict? Social Planning in the Seventies, 'Journal of Social Policy', vol. 10, no. 1 (1981), pp. 31-51.
15. R. Bourne, Joint Social Policy - Or Crowns and Courtiers, 'New Society', 27 November 1975, pp. 473-6.
16. Central Policy Review Staff, 'A Joint Framework for Social Policy' (HMSO, London, 1975).
17. Central Policy Review Staff, 'Population and Social Services' (HMSO, London, 1977); ibid., 'Relations between Central Government and Local Authorities' (HMSO, London, 1977).
18. R. Crossman, 'The Diaries of a Cabinet Minister, Volume 1, Minister of Housing 1964-66' (Hamish Hamilton and Jonathan Cape, London, 1975).
19. H. Heclo and A. Wildavsky, 'The Private Government of Public Money' (Macmillan, London, 1974).
20. R. Smith, 'Joint Approaches to Social Policy at the Local Level' (School for Advanced Urban Studies, mimeo., Bristol, 1978).
21. DHSS, 'A Report from the Working Party on Collaboration between the NHS and Local Government on its Activities to the End of 1972' (HMSO, London, 1973).
22. DHSS, 'The NHS Planning System' (HMSO, London, 1976).
23. Central Policy Review Staff, 'Population and Social Services', p. 8.
24. R. G. S. Brown, 'Reorganising the NHS' (Basil Blackwell and Martin Robertson, Oxford, 1979).
25. G. Wistow and A. Webb, 'Patients First, One Step Backwards for Collaboration' (Loughborough University, Loughborough, 1981).
26. K. Barnard, K. Lee, A. Mills and J. Reynolds, 'Towards a New Rationality: a Study of Planning in the NHS' (The

University of Leeds, Leeds, December 1979).
27. DHSS, 'Patients First' (HMSO, London, 1980).
28. T. A. Booth, Collaboration between the Health and Social Services: Part 1, A Case Study of Joint Care Planning, 'Policy and Politics', vol. 9, no. 1 (1981), pp. 23-49.
29. G. Wistow and S. Head, Pump-Priming Programme, 'Health and Social Service Journal', 3 July 1981, pp. 806-7.
30. S. Lewis, Weaving a Stratagem across Boundaries, 'Health and Social Service Journal', 6 April 1979.
31. S. H. A. Shaw, The Pleasures and Perils of Joint Care Planning, 'Royal Society of Health Journal', vol. 98, no. 4 (1978), pp. 165-72.
32. Brown, 'Reorganising the NHS', p. 156.
33. Booth, Collaboration, p. 32.
34. D. Towell, Giving Fresh Impetus to Collaboration, 'Health and Social Service Journal', 7 August 1981, pp. 964-5.

9 HEALTH PLANNING SYSTEMS: IMPLEMENTATION AND EVALUATION

1 INTRODUCTION

The previous chapters have examined various aspects of health planning and policy-making. This final chapter aims to pull these strands together by looking at the extent to which planning systems actually achieve their objectives. As will be discussed, the gap between policies, plans and their implementation has become a matter of such concern to planners that many planning systems either stress the interdependence of planning and implementation or abandon the word 'planning' in favour of the all-embracing term 'management', in an attempt to remove any dividing line between planning and administration.[1]

A message repeated throughout this book has been that all interested parties cannot be expected to view present or possible future situations in the same way: a conflict of interests and values, whether implicit or explicit, is to be expected in any health sector. It follows that two particular points need to be taken into account in any evaluation of health planning systems. First, different interest groups will have different objectives which they expect to see satisfied via the planning system. Managers may wish to maximise their budget or increase their prestige through acquiring high-technology equipment; doctors may wish to maximise their net income, or prestige, or the number of interesting cases they treat. The Ministry of Health may wish to maximise its control over its peripheral organisations, while these may aim to maximise their autonomy. The government as a whole, especially in a developing country, may use planning to mobilise the people, promote national integration or achieve a political consensus.[2] Consumer organisations may bring pressure to bear on the health service to improve the quality of particular services, or may support the status quo in the face of planners' aims to rationalise services.

Second, any evaluation must take account not only of whose interests are reflected in policies and plans and served by their results, but also of the objectives of the planning system itself. Planning systems are devised, implicitly or explicitly, on the basis of different models of how organisations behave. In a system based on a 'rational' model, a test of a good plan would be that it enables a specified objective to be achieved. However, under 'disjointed incrementalism', the test of a good plan would be that it was agreed by all parties involved.[3] An evaluation of a planning system, therefore, needs also to take into account both the objectives the system was designed to achieve and its assumptions, stated or implied, about the behaviour of organisations.

In consequence, the extent to which plans are implemented is merely one aspect of evaluation. Evaluation also needs to take account of the varying demands made of planning systems; of what they aim to achieve; of the process as well as the outcome of planning; of what the feasible degree of 'rationality' is - in terms of emphasising the analytical and technical components of planning rather than the political component of mediating between various powerful influences.

Accordingly, this chapter looks first at some of the key issues of policy implementation before going on to consider the experience of health planning and its anticipated and realised benefits as these are reflected in the literature. The outline of a methodology for evaluating planning systems is presented, and sections of this are then applied to the NHS planning system. Finally, conclusions on the impact of introducing a planning system into the NHS lead on to a consideration of the prospects for better planning structures and processes to manage change and improve the chances of achieving a desirable future.

2   THE IMPLEMENTATION PHASE

The extent to which a health planning agency is involved in the implementation of plans will depend on the structure of the particular health care system. Three basic models for planning agencies can be distinguished:

(1)   a market approach, where health planners merely oversee the operation of health services by monitoring access and quality and ensuring competition and an informed consumer choice;

(2)   co-operative planning, where agencies have a co-ordinating function; and

(3)   centrally induced or directed planning, where health services are organised and financed publicly and planning agencies possess considerable responsibility and power.

The implicit concern of this book has been primarily with health care systems of the third type. Indeed, the majority of systems fall into this category, though few do not show some signs of the other two approaches. Even in state-directed health care organisations, where planning agencies have in theory considerable authority and legal powers, their use of direct force is, in practice, rare. Successful implementation depends first on knowledge of behaviour and circumstances both within and outside the organisation and of the resources available, and second on the power to carry through decisions.[4] Both knowledge and power are always limited, not absolute. Moreover, the exercise of power is particularly difficult in the medical care sector, where the medical profession has a 'functional monopoly of expertise'.[5] Different health systems are thus likely to encounter similar problems, whenever the centre has some policy-making role, and implementation is the responsibility of peripheral agencies.

Indeed, the larger and more complex the health sector, the greater the likely gap between the enunciation of formal health policy at the centre and whatever is implemented 'on the ground', because different actors have different values and experience and face different influences and pressures. Thus plan implementation is crucial: it is the phase when policy is translated into action. Yet those responsible for implementation are rarely as much involved in policy formulation as the 'formal' policy-makers. In consequence, this latter group cannot assume that the implementors are either sympathetically inclined to follow their wishes or responsive to whatever positive and negative incentives may exist to induce them to comply.

These circumstances leave the formal policy-makers with essentially two options. They can consider the implementation phase to be beyond their remit, or they can attempt to supervise the process and adopt an overtly interventionist posture. In the former case, policy-makers are abdicating any responsibility for effecting changes: policies and plans merely provide 'symbolic reassurance' of central concern and interest. In the latter, policy-makers must concern themselves with activities at the periphery, and ensure that a reporting system exists to inform the centre on the extent to which performance reflects the original policy intent and to enable corrective action to be taken when necessary. As Chapter 6 showed, policy-making and planning in the NHS has provided over the last ten years or so material evidence of the importance of these points.

3 THE EXPERIENCE OF HEALTH PLANNING

Any evaluation of a health planning system must start, of necessity, with the identification of the benefits the system was intended to achieve and whether, over a period of time, these benefits have been realised. Chapter 2 identified some of the hoped-for benefits of health planning systems adopted in the UK and USA, and advocated by the World Health Organization.

However, despite the world-wide adoption of health planning, considerable pessimism exists in the research literature on the extent to which health planning systems have proved themselves to be worthwhile. One review of the literature concluded: 'there is a notable lack of evidence that planning is effective in accomplishing specified outcomes, and it is also clear that intended processes have been subverted in some instances.'[6] Another review, of 33 completed health plans in the US, concluded that most plans lacked a description of the health service framework desired at the end of the planning period; devoted scant attention to formulation and selection of alternative long-range goals and short-range objectives; used very little information or analysis to justify their stated priorities; and failed to specify dates for the implementation of recommendations.[7]

Such pessimism about the impact of planning does not appear to be confined to the health sector or to the United States. For instance, an extensive study of development planning concluded that many countries had abandoned their medium-term plans and that, in general, plans were facades, ignored or circumvented by sector Ministries, with real power being wielded by budgetary authorities.[8] In Kenya, a study of the extent to which the Kenyan third five-year plan had been implemented concluded that Kenya's considerable economic progress since independence may owe rather little to the existence of planning machinery; and that a good deal of the expertise and other resources devoted to the preparation of five-year planning documents had an unnecessarily low social productivity.[9] Indeed, some writers have argued that planning - whether social, economic or strategic - is losing its credibility, and in many circles planning has been severely attacked and denounced as an expensive and even pernicious approach to tackling the complex problems of present-day societies.[10]

Thus, while the planning industry is continuing to thrive, especially in the developing world, considerable disillusionment with planning also exists, especially in some developed countries. A number of viewpoints are apparent: some writers feel that planning has yet to be given a fair trial; others that existing institutions and infrastructures need to be improved for planning to succeed; others that planning models themselves need to be re-fashioned; yet others that environmental and behavioural constraints make the aims of planning unrealisable.

All these views might be said to constitute a conventional, if critical, view of planning. In addition, a radical view of health planning is emerging in both the US and UK, which questions the motivations of those who advocate health planning. This view argues that advocates of rational comprehensive planning misleadingly portray planning as an objective science, performed by rational people, uninfluenced by interest group or ideological biases. It is more realistic to assume that not all participants in planning are equal, and that health planning methods are not neutral but rather value-laden, providing mechanisms for particular interest groups to affect the delivery of health services. Hence, in these terms, health planning is to be seen as an ideology, compatible with the dominant set of beliefs of powerful interest groups, and designed to support existing power relations.[11] The language of rational comprehensive planning provides credibility, and together with mechanisms for the involvement - but not participation - of various groups in decision-making, increases the chances of implementation.

In summary, therefore, two contrasting judgements on the operation of health planning systems exist. The one sees planning as a response to the scale and complexity of health issues, providing an information system, a means of co-ordination and a framework for making difficult choices. The other sees planning as essentially to do with control, as an ideological cover for strengthening or maintaining existing dominant interests.

4 APPROACHES TO THE EVALUATION OF HEALTH PLANNING SYSTEMS

The evaluation of planning systems has been approached in a variety of ways, and according to different criteria. One approach is to evaluate the extent to which planners have achieved their targets.[12] But this is not so simple a task as it might at first appear, since it implies the consideration of what would have happened in the absence of planning, and assessment of what results should be attributed to the planning element in planned decisions when most decisions are made under conditions of uncertainty, and are affected by many variables. These problems have led some writers to argue that planning should not be judged by its results, but in terms of the extent to which planning increases the probability of improving decisions and solving problems.[13] This second approach, therefore, stresses the evaluation of the planning process rather than of its outcome.

Hence, in any attempted evaluation, it would appear necessary first to explore the meanings of the terms 'process' and 'outcome' of planning. 'Outcomes' can be considered at different levels or stages of planning. The production of a health plan can be regarded as an outcome of the planning process; but equally, the logic of the whole planning system implies that the plan will result in a change in service activity and, beyond that, will have an impact on the health status of the population. Similarly, three different 'processes' can be distinguished: the act of planning itself, the implementation of the plan and the management of a new or modified activity. Processes and outcomes can thus be portrayed in the following way:

A. PROCESS B. OUTCOME
A1 Planning B1 The Plan
A2 Plan implementation B2 Change in service activity
A3 Management of a new B3 Impact on health status
   or revised activity

Architects of planning systems are likely to attach different importance to these various aspects of planning. Thus, for instance, those who emphasise the process of planning more than the final results of planning will concentrate their design of a planning system on the stages of A1 and B1. Those who see planning as primarily a system of control to support dominant interests would emphasise A1 through to B2. And those who see the major objective of the health plan to be the maximisation of health status would stress A3 and B3. Emphasis on particular stages does not necessarily mean total exclusion of any one stage. Stressing B3 implies that the earlier stages, especially A1 and B1, should include an emphasis on the analytical and technical components of planning. Furthermore, an undue emphasis on the planning process to the virtual exclusion of outcomes is likely to be counter-productive, for it can be argued that unless planning has a visible result, and one that is intended by planners, the members of any organisation are likely to become frustrated and unwilling to devote time and energy to planning.

It could, of course, be argued that to adopt such a wide methodology for evaluation goes far beyond evaluating the planning system itself. In defence, it can be argued that there is more to planning than the production of a plan, and since a gap frequently exists between planning and implementation, the evaluator is obliged to enquire about the implementation of the plan and its impact on the target population.

5 EVALUATION OF THE NHS PLANNING SYSTEM: A PROPOSED METHODOLOGY

In this section, this evaluation methodology is amplified in the context of the NHS planning system. The objectives and main features of the system are analysed, and a model set up for evaluation by attaching the characteristics demanded by the formal planning system to each of the stages of 'process' and 'outcome'. In the next section, this model is applied to illustrate how well particular aspects of the NHS planning system have operated in practice.

The objectives and characteristics of the NHS planning system have been set out in various DHSS publications, notably in the NHS Planning Manual [14] and in subsequent guidance[15]:

(1) 'effective planning [is] the means of improving

170

decision-making and managing resources'[16]

(2) 'the planning system is intended to help in changing attitudes to the provision and distribution of health services'[17]

(3) 'the purpose of [strategic] planning is to achieve in the foreseeable future a coherent pattern of service development and resource deployment, designed to ensure the most cost-effective use of all available resources for the benefit of those who use the service'[18]

(4) 'the potential benefits are clear: they include an objective and factual information base for making decisions; a better definition of the various responsibilities of those involved in providing health care, and better lines of communication between them; and a clear understanding of what can and cannot be achieved both locally and nationally given the expected levels of resources. These will, in turn, enable NHS management to be both flexible and positive - qualities which are essential for an organisation as complex as the NHS to reassess, redeploy and develop its services.'[19]

(5) 'above all, perhaps, the [planning] systems are intended as systems of communication: they should enable policy-making at the centre to be carried out with the benefit of comprehensive information on problems, needs, and resources from the field, and for local decision-makers to act in the context of comprehensive national policies on service provision'[20]

(6) 'the test of the usefulness of the planning systems will not be the paper - guidelines and plans - which they produce, valuable as this may be; rather it will be the extent to which better informed and more rational decisions are made on providing the best services given the resources available'[21]

(7) 'health care planning [should] be comprehensive . . . and co-ordinated . . . it must be corporate'[22]

(8) 'whilst planning needs to be flexible enough to accommodate these changing patterns of need, it must also be directed towards removing the existing substantial inequalities of care and provision'[23]

(9) 'the selective allocation of resources is only acceptable if the criteria used for selectivity are seen to be objective and fair . . . such decisions should be arrived at on an information basis which is as objective and factual as possible'[24]

(10) 'to achieve the broad aim of improving the performance of the entire health service in meeting the nation's health needs, planning will have to be responsive to certain criteria: relevance to needs;

relevance to supply; realism; consultation; compatibility; flexibility; comprehensive'.[25]

From these various statements, a list of the objectives and characteristics of the NHS planning system has been developed and related to the various stages of 'process' and 'outcome'. It appears as Figure 4. Some characteristics are attached to more than one stage, since they are expected to be visible at various stages in the planning system. For instance, 'realism' should, according to the planning model, pervade the planning process, as well as be evident in the plan. It is clear from studying Figure 4 that the characteristics desired cluster in the first two boxes (A1 and B1), suggesting that the DHSS has given most attention to the planning process and to the nature and content of the plan. This is not unexpected, since the processes of implementation and managing new activities are tasks for which procedures have always existed and which are regularly undertaken by administrators. Yet it is notable that relatively little attention has been given to incorporating health status considerations in the planning system, or to monitoring the results of plans in terms of their impact on the health of the community. In contrast, considerable stress is laid on efficiency, realism and control.

A problem faced by this evaluation methodology is that many of the characteristics listed are qualitative not quantitative, lack precision and demand definition before any attempt can be made to identify the extent to which they feature in planning. Many of the hypotheses developed to help explain observed behaviour will thus at first sight be untestable directly. However, they will enable predictions to be made that are testable and can be used to challenge the hypotheses.[26] For instance, the question can be put: if the planning system has improved decision-making, what characteristics of the decision-making process and of decisions would one expect to see? Indicators can then be devised to shape the gathering and analysis of data.

6   THE OPERATION OF THE NHS PLANNING SYSTEM

Introduction

It may be that to compare planning behaviour in England with statements of DHSS expectations is to apply too severe a test. For instance, architects of the system might well argue that certain aspects have a symbolic value, or are intended to promote particular attitudes rather than specific actions. The counter-argument is that the planning system has raised expectations by its claims and entails considerable time and effort. It should therefore not be excused a comprehensive evaluation of whether it has had the desired results, and led

A. PROCESS

Process	Characteristics
A1 PLANNING	– change attitudes – corporate – realism – consultation – co-ordinated – objective/factual – act as communication system – improve decision-making
A2 PLAN IMPLEMENTATION	– consultation
A3 MANAGE NEW/REVISED ACTIVITIES	

B. OUTCOME

Outcome	Characteristics
B1 THE PLAN	– related to guidelines – act as communication system – equitable – relevant to supply constraints – realistic – cost-effective – relevant to needs – compatible – flexible – comprehensive – co-ordinated – objective/factual
B2 CHANGE IN SERVICE ACTIVITY	– cost-effective – improvement in service – remedy inequalities – meet needs
B3 IMPACT ON HEALTH STATUS	

to changes that were intended. Accordingly, in this section, an evaluation of two stages of the NHS planning system is presented, namely the Planning Process (A1) and its Impact on Health Status (B3). The material is drawn mainly from the results of the authors' three-year study of the NHS planning system, which was largely based on detailed research in two English Health Authorities.[27] The aim in presenting this material is, first, to report research findings and, second, to demonstrate the potential of the methodology set out earlier in this chapter. The evaluation is confined, for reasons of space, to only two of the six stages of the evaluation model.

The Planning Process (A1)

Figure 4 indicates that official documents expected the planning process to possess certain characteristics. It is important, therefore, to consider whether each of these characteristics was evident in planning behaviour.

Attitude Change. The measurement of attitude change is an extremely complex task and, from a methodological point of view, suggests that some form of 'before and after' study is necessary. None the less, some general points can be offered. There was a high degree of acceptance amongst NHS managers of the philosophy and concepts of the planning system - at least in the 1970s. Managers could see themselves as 'corporate rationalisers'[28], viewing planning as a mechanism for systematising and controlling the behaviour of the organisation, and as a test of their own abilities. Many NHS officers showed that they were prepared to put these views into practice in their attempts to ensure that all activities relating to future developments were firmly controlled within the planning system, even though many also felt that the mechanics of the system were often complicated and time-consuming. Yet, at the same time, frustration was apparent, caused by the success some interest groups had in bypassing the planning system and visibly demonstrating that unreserved acceptance of planning had not permeated all levels of the NHS. As Chapter 7 showed, individuals and groups did not always perceive it to be in their best interests to work through the planning system and if they were sufficiently powerful, NHS officers were obliged to acquiesce.

Corporate Planning. The degree to which planning is corporate is indicated by the extent to which medical and other staff interests, key officers at any one level and managers of all levels are involved in NHS planning. In a service that employs nearly one million people, the involvement of all staff interests is necessarily going to be less than total. Corporate planning therefore demands suitable forums for discussion, well organised means for ensuring the expression of views or representation of interest groups and reliable communication systems. As Chapter 7 discussed in detail, medical staff were involved to a greater extent than any other staff group and it often proved both difficult and time-consuming to ensure even that information on service changes was disseminated adequately to all staff.

The close involvement of key officers at the management levels of Area or Region was hampered by professional boundaries between officers of different disciplines and by the management structure. Administrative planners tended to predominate over planners of other disciplines such as community medicine or nursing. Attempts to bring officers together in multidisciplinary planning teams encountered a variety of obstacles. In particular, the management structure laid down centrally by the DHSS discouraged, unintentionally, the delegation of planning tasks to second-in-line teams [29] and thus made it difficult for such teams to create a distinct role for themselves and define their responsibilities vis-à-vis the team of chief officers. Inter-tier corporate planning encountered even greater difficulties. The planning system, by distributing planning responsibilities between the tiers, had demanded a high degree of co-ordination which was undermined by rivalries and conflicts (as discussed in Chapter 6). The conclusions of the research, therefore, were that effective corporate planning hinged on the interests of the various groups involved being not too divergent, and that corporate planning was by no means costless and could result in slow and lengthy decision-making, or even a stalemate. In consequence, corporate planning was an ideal to aim at for some managers, or an occasional necessary expedient for others, rather than the norm of planning behaviour in practice.

Realism. Plans can be 'realistic' in at least two senses: plans that are feasible in physical and resource terms; and plans that are politically feasible. Neither interpretation offers clear-cut rules to planners. In its first sense, financial realism, for example, was not a clear concept since resource assumptions were rarely firm and extra resources could be allocated at short notice. Moreover, it was not necessarily in an Authority's interest to adhere to resource guidelines: plans were not only a means of setting priorities and managing budgets, but also a bid for resources that might be allocated elsewhere. It could therefore be realistic to plan for a higher level of expenditure than that forecast, and politically prudent to include in plans an element of overbidding for resources.

Consultation. On the whole, Authorities were careful to observe the formal consultation procedures. However, following the formalities did not ensure that these were found to be satisfactory by all parties involved. Consultation on strategic, or even operational, plans tended to create little lasting interest, but consultation on specific issues could arouse much greater interest (see Chapter 7). Considerable frustration could develop when the Authority was not seen to be responsive to comments, and over major issues, where adversaries could mobilise sufficient support, they attempted to turn the consultative process into negotiations. In consequence, the crucial period for reaching agreement on plans was often not so much the period of consultation during the planning process as the implementation phase. Interested parties who might be relatively quiet initially could mobilise support rapidly when the issue became more immediate. Consultation was thus one of the most difficult and crucial aspects of the planning process, requiring managers and planners to possess considerable political skills.

Co-ordinated. Co-ordination of local authority and NHS plans achieved some successes, though for reasons already discussed in Chapter 8 DHSS pronouncements on collaboration were clearly unrealistic. It would be naïve to blame the collaborative structure for the lack of co-ordination of the planning process: while intentions were often honourable, in practice insufficient incentives existed to produce collaboration. In many respects, co-ordination was peripheral to the major concerns of Authorities, and it was more likely to be at District (i.e. local) level that interest existed to improve co-ordination, principally to tackle planning issues in the context of operational problems.

Objective/Factual. 'Objectivity' was a cause popular amongst NHS planners, many considering that an objective, factual analysis should underlie plans. However, the recommended planning process of taking stock, setting objectives and defining strategies was not one followed either scrupulously or consistently in the two Authorities. Stock was taken of particular services that were a source of concern; objectives were not set systematically, and tended to be couched in terms of desirable patterns of facilities rather than the satisfaction of population needs; strategies did not often include a very systematic consideration of options, but rather tended to be expressed in terms of capital developments. Decision-makers relied heavily during the formulation of plans on general intelligence, expert opinion and logical thinking. This is not to say that quantitative information was unimportant: indeed, a considerable amount of data was collected, analysed and used. However, this information tended to be used more to justify decisions than to make them. In essence, 'objectivity' needed to be matched with political realism. In some circumstances, no amount of factual analysis could bridge the gap between opposing interests when their respective positions were based on different value systems (see Chapter 5).

Communication System. A system of communications depends vitally on whether activities are conducted openly. Yet whether the results of the various stages of the planning process are made explicit or not will depend to a great extent on whether officers perceive 'openness' to be in their interests. Sufficient evidence exists to indicate that there was a tendency towards secrecy - associated with not revealing trump cards or unwelcome news too early - except when it was felt that to conceal would incur higher penalties than to reveal.

Improved Decision-making. 'Improving decision-making' is by no means a value-free or clear-cut yardstick though, as argued earlier, it should be possible to identify indicators of whether or not the planning process affected the quality of decision-making. The merits of publishing a plan and seeking views via the consultation process were that it effectively placed officers in a position where they had to justify their decisions. To this extent, therefore, there was a greater degree of public accountability and debate; and the division of planning tasks within the NHS obliged each tier to justify its plans to the next tier. Yet, at the same time, there was considerable evidence that this process could lead to very protracted negotiations, and to delays in resolving difficult planning issues. What is less clear, however, is whether such delays were not as much a result of the complexity of the NHS structure and of increasing financial stringency as of the planning system per se.[30]

Impact on Health Status (B3)

Planners operating in accordance with a rational comprehensive approach would consider it all-important to have as their ultimate objective the improvement of health status, and hence ought to make a conscious effort to formulate plans and measure their effectiveness in such terms. It has already been noted that while the DHSS Planning Manual emphasised planning as the means to achieve efficiency and cost-effectiveness for the benefit of consumers[31], no explicit discussion of how benefits might be defined was included. This avoidance of consideration of the impact of plans upon the overall health status of communities was reflected subsequently in local plans whose objectives were expressed largely in terms of reaching norms of provision (in numbers of beds or staff), of changing throughput or utilisation rates, or of introducing new capital schemes. While health status was recognised to be the ultimate concern of planners, little or no attempt seemed to be made to translate this concern into operational terms, to define or measure states of health or to assess by what activities these might best be improved.

Of course, there are obvious difficulties to be faced in identifying and measuring changes in health status. Moreover, the selection of an appropriate criterion by which a plan could be judged to have maximised health status is not straightforward. Three criteria are relevant:

(1) efficiency - aiming to maximise a specified output from a service at a given cost;

(2) effectiveness - aiming to produce a favourable change in the state of health of the population through service or other activities; or

(3) equity - aiming to change the distribution or take-up of services, or (which should follow) to reduce the disparities in health status, between regions, age groups, sexes and health care or client groups.

Yet these criteria are not necessarily compatible with each other. Thus if the criterion is efficiency, and resources are allocated in order to make the most efficient use of existing health facilities, the effect may well be different from that which would result from adopting a criterion of equity. In this latter case, attention may be focused on improving the health status of a deprived section of the population, with efficiency being a secondary criterion. In other words, the 'allocative efficiency' criterion takes second place to the 'distributive efficiency' criterion. Or, yet again, the aim may be to develop a health service which concentrates its activities on treatment regimes of proven clinical effectiveness and hence on those conditions which are most amenable to treatment. This may well be questioned by those concerned that the service will become less available to other groups in the population whose needs cannot be measured or met in such terms. Notions of clinical effectiveness and availability may thus conflict, suggesting that, in terms of planning, societies may be as interested in deciding who receives treatment and hence who is kept waiting or denied, as in selecting the more effective forms of treatment.

Ultimately, the choice of criteria will depend upon whose perspective and perception is taken. Just as it is quite possible that what is perceived to be a 'good plan' by planners may not be so regarded by providers, so it is possible that when a health authority considers that its long-term plans will lead to a significant improvement in the health and well-being of its population, the plans may not be welcomed by those community interests who value differently the expected benefits.

7 THE NHS PLANNING SYSTEM: A COMMENTARY

The previous section attempted to measure the behaviour of the NHS planning system against the official model. If the analysis indicated a considerable gap between theory and practice and was critical of the operation of the system, the explanation should be sought not only in the 'irrationality', according to the standards of the planning model, of NHS behaviour, but also in the inappropriateness of the planning model to the NHS. How closely does the NHS planning system come, in both its design and its practice, to any of the planning models and theories discussed in earlier chapters? A historical perspective of planning in the NHS suggests that for much of its history incrementalism was the preferred mode of decision-making. Thus Maddox [32] described decision-making in the late 1960s as disjointed incrementalism on the grounds that only minor adjustments in policy occurred, and that the complex administrative structure made it more likely that partisans would contest and politicise all questions of consequence. Reorganisation in 1974 and the introduction of the NHS planning system in 1975/6 were expected to change this and introduce a greater element of conscious planning, as well as a greater responsiveness both to the policies of the centre and to local circumstances. In short, the language of the planning system conformed closely to the rational comprehensive model.

However, experience suggests that Authorities have been moving only slowly from disjointed incrementalism towards mixed scanning as the NHS planning system takes root, some issues being analysed in depth while others are subject to only incremental changes. None the less, while this represents the broad picture, there have been occasions when Authorities appeared to resemble rational comprehensive planners, on other occasions mixed scanners, and at yet other times disjointed incrementalists. Can it be predicted under what conditions an Authority will act in a particular way?

Friedmann has stated that 'technical' planning is important where goals are clear, widely held and deemed to be important; when system performance is believed to depart significantly from the norm; and when expert judgement plus a variety of control mechanisms is held to be more effective than political manipulation.[33] Given these criteria, it is not surprising that in the case of the NHS, where agreement on objectives is lacking, values vary widely and many groups claim a right to be involved in decisions, the rational comprehensive model is rarely seen in practice.

Furthermore, the ability of the planner to offer even technical advice has been questioned by those who argue that rational planning is based on the illusion that it is possible to anticipate the future needs or circumstances of society ten to twenty years ahead. This is the argument that supports the disjointed incrementalist's approach, for a tendency towards incremental and sequential policy changes, correcting and adjusting at each step, has long been recognised as a highly effective means of proceeding under conditions of uncertainty.[34] The danger, however, as outlined in Chapter

3, is that such adjustment may frustrate the capacity of society to recognise or tackle 'higher-level' problems where radical change may be the required response.

It is possible to discern within the NHS a tendency to adopt a rational comprehensive approach in respect only of long-term plans, where decisions on implementation lie some distance into the future and where changes do not immediately threaten to disrupt established patterns of behaviour. Long-term issues can be dealt with at a fairly high level of generalisation, and arouse the minimum of conflict and dissent. In contrast, short-term plans can be seen to be influenced more by a mixed scanning approach, where attention is concentrated on, and solutions sought for, a narrow range of problems. Yet even here, practice falls short of the model of mixed scanning, for the analytical work done is still comparatively limited: norms and expert opinion, rather than any detailed analysis of needs, demands and resources, have been relied on. At the point of implementation, disjointed incrementalism is most apparent. For instance, unforeseen events such as extra allocations of resources during the year have demanded the rapid development of suitable projects, often outside the framework of the plan. Cuts in services to keep within cash limits have been dealt with often in like manner, at least until local managers were satisfied that the revenue shortfall was not a temporary phenomenon.

It is implicit within this analysis that long-term plans do not necessarily remain unchanged through to implementation. Both opportunism and necessity have made planners recognise that plans cannot be considered sacrosanct and that changed circumstances can be an open invitation for dissatisfied parties to attempt to renegotiate and bargain.

8 THE FUTURE OF PLANNING

Finally, given these observed trends, is it possible to come to any conclusions on the success or otherwise of the NHS planning system, and do these conclusions suggest factors which are likely to affect the ability of any planning system to govern the future? It is helpful to structure the discussion in terms of the four basic assumptions about health planning detailed in Chapter 2.

Political Stability

For more than thirty years there has been broad agreement with the basic principles of the NHS. These principles have included universal access, finance predominantly from general taxation, services free at the point of consumption and public ownership of hospitals and health centres. In brief, the objective of the NHS has been to make available a complete range of medical services to the people of Britain, irrespective of their financial or health status. No British political party, at least whilst in office, was prepared or inclined until the early 1980s to risk the political damage that might have resulted from changing the well established concept of a free health service for all. It has yet to be seen whether the Conservative government's interest in health insurance will be translated into a substantial alteration in the financing of health services.

The consequence of this broad agreement on basic principles has been that political debate on the NHS has centred upon the form and structure of the NHS organisation and, though mainly in recent years, on the policies and priorities that the NHS should implement. Indeed, structural changes have frequently been seen as the solution to perceived service deficiencies and such proposals have created uncertainty and tension within the NHS. Yet the limited impact of the structural changes that have been implemented is implied by the fact that changes in NHS spending patterns in the last thirty years have been slight. This resistance to change in the pattern of services suggests that the informal political structure and the stability through time of accustomed relationships and styles of behaviour have diminished the likelihood of large-scale change in medical priorities.

In the context of other countries, the lesson to be learnt is that policies and plans are acceptable only if the values upon which they are based are also acceptable, and that the health sector cannot necessarily expect to remain unaffected by politics. Hence, any changes in government at a central or local level may threaten the content of policies and plans. Whether any change in policy affects the delivery of services will depend on the effectiveness of the line of command from centre to periphery, and on the responsiveness of local staff. Planning, given its emphasis on the future, requires some degree of political stability though, as in England, this itself may impede the achievement of radical change.

Economic Stability

Uncertainty about future resource availability might not be expected to figure as a major impediment to policy-making and planning in a developed country such as England. The NHS managed, over its first thirty years, to more than double its real spending and to increase by nearly 50 per cent its proportion of the GNP. Yet, throughout this period, accusations that the NHS was under-funded continued unabated. While some domestic commentators have seen shortage of resources as a purely British phenomenon attributable to public funding, it is clear that all countries search for ways in which policies and plans can be developed to reconcile unlimited needs with finite resources, in such a way that instabilities in revenue from year to year do not result.

Even if stability of the total health budget of a country can be guaranteed, it does not necessarily follow that stability is assured at the local level. Indeed, within the NHS, health authorities have found changing resource assumptions and lack of long-term resource guidelines to be a major problem. The accumulation of a number of factors, each on its own fairly minor, can create considerable uncertainty. In the NHS, these have included the impact of national resource redeployment and reallocation policies, the imposition of cash limits and uncertainty on likely inflation rates, the distribution of unexpected cash windfalls and local resistance to change leading to delays in realising savings from hospital closures. When plans concentrate on planning for extra resources, as they tend to however much budgeting is encouraged to be zero-based, small variations in allocations can have a major impact on plan implementation.

In general, it can be assumed that in an uncertain or worsening financial climate, governments will tend to adopt tactics that make it extremely difficult for planning authorities to predict future resource availability. This argument appears to be as relevant in Britain [35] as it has been shown to be for developing countries.[36] Whether, however, financial stringency promotes more planning and greater rationality, or more conflict and a less considered analysis of priorities, is debatable. Rightly or wrongly, many participants in planning consider additional financial resources to be the necessary currency for changes to take place. A major shortage of resources provides the opportunity and the necessity for a radical reappraisal of services, but at the same time the anticipated level of conflict between interested parties may be too high for such a reappraisal to take place.

Will and Compliance

Any centrally funded health care system has to reconcile political and financial accountability to the government of the day with a recognition that national policies need to take account of the views of staff at the local level, and indeed to profit from their experience and knowledge. The pluralist nature of NHS decision-making means that an acknowledgement of the influence key actors have on policy-making is critical to the success of any health plan. As has been demonstrated, although central government can alter the flow of funds into the system, the effective translation of plans into a set of actions in specific locations still depends upon the behaviour of the individuals and groups who have the power to affect positively or negatively the pace of policy implementation. At the macro level, therefore, a major issue is whether a health planning system can be both a system of control (which implies a degree of rigidity and the availability of sanctions) and a local management tool to encourage innovative thinking, initiative and local self-reliance.

At a micro level, an organisation the size of the NHS is bound to experience internal conflict at one point or another in its structure: indeed, it could be argued that some organisational tension is healthy. Among the key issues raised has been whether the involvement of interest groups in the process of planning will enable those whose needs have been neglected to exercise much effective leverage on the organisation against established professional and political interests. The analysis of NHS experience has raised some doubts on this point, but has also shown that compromises are continuously being made between conflicting interests. The conclusion drawn is that, given the different value systems that exist within and outside the NHS, the most profitable form of policy-making and planning behaviour will include negotiation as an important strategy.[37] The implication of this conclusion for a planning system is that strategies which result in successful implementation may be rather different from those designed for 'rational planning'.

An important safeguard in a health planning system such as that of the NHS is the public nature of local plans, and the opportunities provided by consultative procedures for the expression of views. In some countries and some contexts these safeguards will be considered quite inadequate to ensure that the pattern of health services is tailored to the needs and demands of the majority of consumers, rather than to the needs of elites or providers. In others they will represent the means of ensuring the accountability of policy-makers and planners to some form of local constituency.

Technical Infrastructure

The implications of the limitless need (and demand) for health services is that choice must be exercised on who should receive what care. The case for health planning is that such choice is unlikely to be enlightened, efficient or effective in the absence of an explicit process for generating policies, developing plans and implementing decisions. Hence, it can be argued that some form of planning is worth while, as a means of coping with uncertainty, of anticipating difficulties and of determining the appropriate time-scale for taking decisions. Yet even if a form of planning is available, the question remains as to whether and under what circumstances it is likely to be used to shape decisions.

Perhaps not surprisingly, few decisions are taken on the basis of analytical findings alone. Indeed, in the context of the NHS planning system, it was not at all evident that quantitative information, where it did exist, had a major impact on planning decisions. Information based on tradition, intuition and wisdom was as, or even more, important. Furthermore, while the development of standardised documentation for plans was considered to be an essential element of the NHS planning system, it did not of itself ensure that planning forms were completed, or that planning was shaped in the desired way. A lack of planners, techniques or methodologies was not the main problem: a lack of incentives and in some cases considerable opposition to any new approach were far more serious factors. In short, it is difficult to escape the conclusion that the application of analytical frameworks and skills depends in large measure on the nature of the political environment within which policy-making and planning take place. Analysts thus need to develop the political awareness of when their skills and techniques are appropriate, and how they can be used in such a way as to maximise their impact on decision-makers. This is crucial if decisions are to be technically sound as well as politically acceptable.

Conclusion

In our concluding remarks, we are reluctant to reduce planning to the true cynics' aphorisms: 'human nature is always problematic especially where people are concerned' and 'Forecasting is always difficult, but particularly where it concerns the future', but they do reinforce the essential message. Planning does not guarantee a desired future: it is a way of exploring the possibility of one. How that exploration is conducted depends on the people involved. In a complex environment like the health sector, it is unreasonable not to expect that individuals and groups have different values, interests and territories to defend. Policy-making and planning then have to handle that complexity and conflict, and different approaches will be relevant in different situations. Where resource assumptions are highly unstable, detailed long-term planning will be impracticable and long-term plans may at best provide the context for short-term decision-making. Even medium- or short-term plans will need to incorporate flexibility and avoid the dangers of 'blueprint' planning. In certain circumstances, a focus on improving the annual budgetary process, to make it more sensitive to demands for efficiency and equity, may be more appropriate than the introduction of a planning system as such. Whenever time and skills are in short supply, a strategy of selectivity, or mixed scanning, to pick out and concentrate on urgent and major problems is likely to be more 'rational'.

Health planning has unfortunately been damaged by the exaggerated expectations aroused by comprehensive, corporate planning systems and the adoption, knowingly or otherwise, of a false unitary belief in a single rationality within the health sector. It is not too simplistic, we believe, to conclude that efforts should be made towards a 'new rationality', one that accepts diversity and conflict within and between health agencies, but attempts to minimise their potentially disruptive effects and seeks to harness them for the improvement of health services and of health itself.

NOTES

1. WHO, 'Guiding Principles for the Managerial Process for National Health Development' (WHO, Geneva, 1980).
2. J. Friedmann, A Conceptual Model for the Analysis of Planning Behaviour, 'Administrative Science Quarterly' (1967), pp. 225-52.
3. C. E. Lindblom, The Science of 'Muddling Through', 'Public Administration Review', vol. 19 (Spring 1959).
4. A. Faludi, 'Planning Theory' (Pergamon Press, Oxford, 1973), Chapter 15.
5. R. Klein, Policy-making in the National Health Service, 'Political Studies', vol. XXII, no. 1 (1974), p. 6.
6. N. Anderson and L. Robins, Observations on Potential Contributions of Health Planning, 'International Journal of Health Services', vol. 6, no. 4 (1976).
7. N. J. Frieden and J. Peters, Urban Planning and Health Services: Opportunities for Co-operation, 'Journal of the American Institute of Planners', vol. 36, no. 2 (1970), pp. 82-95.
8. A. Waterston, An Operational Approach to Development Planning, 'International Journal of Health Services', vol. 1, no. 3 (1971), pp. 233-52.
9. T. Killick and J. K. Kinyua, On Implementing Development Plans: a Case Study, 'ODI Review', no. 1 (1980).
10. Y. Manor and G. Sheffer, Can Planning be Salvaged?, 'Public Administration', vol. 55 (Summer 1977).
11. E. A. Krause, Health Planning as a Managerial Ideology, 'International Journal of Health Services', vol. 3, no. 3 (1973); L. Tannen, Health Planning as a Regulatory Strategy: a Discussion of its History and Current Uses, 'International Journal of Health Services', vol. 10, no. 1 (1980); H. Glennerster, From Containment to Conflict? Social Planning in the Seventies, 'Journal of Social Policy', vol. 10, no. 1 (1981), pp. 31-51.
12. See, for instance, Killick and Kinyua, On Implementing Development Plans, pp. 30-3.
13. Manor and Sheffer, Can Planning be Salvaged?, pp. 218-9.
14. DHSS, 'The NHS Planning System' (HMSO, London, 1976).
15. DHSS, 'Background Paper on Planning in the DHSS and NHS', RCP2 (1977).
16. 'NHS Planning System', p. 3.
17. Ibid.

18. Ibid., p. 12.
19. 'Background Paper', p. 6.
20. Ibid., p. 2.
21. Ibid., p. 6.
22. 'NHS Planning System', p. 3.
23. Ibid.
24. Ibid.
25. Ibid., p. 4.
26. W. Belson, Social Surveys: Pitfalls and Potential, 'Journal of the Royal Society of Arts' (May 1977), pp. 306-16.
27. K. Barnard, K. Lee, A. Mills and J. Reynolds, 'Towards a New Rationality: a Study of Planning in the National Health Service', vols. I-IV (The University of Leeds, Leeds, December 1979).
28. R. Alford, 'Health Care Politics' (University of Chicago Press, Chicago, 1975).
29. K. Barnard, K. Lee, A. Mills and J. Reynolds, NHS Planning: an Assessment, Parts 1 and 2, 'Hospital and Health Services Review' (August and September 1980).
30. K. Barnard, K. Lee and J. Reynolds, 'Tracing Decisions in the NHS' (King's Fund Publication RC16, 1981).
31. DHSS, 'NHS Planning System', p. 15.
32. G. L. Maddox, Muddling Through: Planning for Health Care in England, 'Medical Care', vol. IX, no. 5 (1972), pp. 439-48.
33. Friedmann, Conceptual Model, p. 234.
34. K. Lee, Health Care: Planning, Policies and Incentives, 'Futures', vol. 11, no. 6 (1979).
35. H. Glennerster, Prime Cuts: Public Expenditure and Social Services Planning in a Hostile Environment, 'Policy and Politics', vol. 8, no. 4 (1980), pp. 367-82.
36. N. Caiden and A. Wildavsky, 'Planning and Budgeting in Poor Countries' (John Wiley and Sons, New York, 1974).
37. Barnard et al., 'NHS Planning', p. 303.

Abel-Smith, B., and Leiserson, A. Poverty, Development, and Health Policy in 'Public Health Paper 69' (WHO, Geneva, 1978).
-- Health Care in a Cold Economic Climate, 'The Lancet', 14 February 1981.
Alaszewski, A., Tether, P., and McDonnell, H. Another Dose of Managerialism? - Commentary on the Consultative Paper 'Patients First', 'Social Science and Medicine', vol. 15A (1981).
Alford, A. 'Health Care Politics' (University of Chicago Press, Chicago, 1975).
Allen, D. 'Hospital Planning' (Pitman Medical, Tunbridge Wells, 1979).
Anderson, N., and Robins, L. Observations on Potential Contributions of Health Planning, 'International Journal of Health Services', vol. 6, no. 4 (1976).
Arnstein, S. R. A Ladder of Citizen Participation, 'American Institute of Planners Journal' (July 1969).
Atkinson, A. B., and Stiglitz, J. E. Theories of the State and Public Economics, 'Lectures on Public Economics' (McGraw-Hill, New York, 1980).
Babson, J. H. 'Disease Costing' (Manchester University Press, Manchester, 1973).
Bachrach, P., and Baratz, M. S. The Two Faces of Power, 'American Political Science Review', vol. 56 (1972).
Banfield, E. C. Ends and Means in Planning, 'International Social Science Journal', vol. XI, no. 3 (1959).
Banks, G. T., et al. 'Planning, Programming, Budgeting System for the Health and Social Services' (DHSS, London, 1971).
Banks, G. T. Programme Budgeting in the DHSS in T. A. Booth (ed.), 'Planning for Welfare: Social Policy and the Expenditure Process' (Basil Blackwell and Martin Robertson, Oxford, 1979).
Barnard, K. Comprehensive Health Planning - the State of the Art, 'Community Medicine', vol. 129, no. 19 (1973).
-- Health Planning: the Last of the Panaceas in K. Barnard and K. Lee (eds.), 'NHS Reorganisation: Issues and Prospects' (The University of Leeds, Leeds, 1974).
--, Lee K., Mills, A., and Reynolds, J. 'Towards a New Rationality: a Study of Planning in the National Health Service', vols. I-IV inclusive (The University of Leeds,

Leeds, December 1979).

--, --, --, --, NHS Planning: an Assessment, 'Hospital and Health Services Review' (August 1980).

--, --, --, --, NHS Planning: an Assessment Concluded, 'Hospital and Health Services Review' (September 1980).

--, Lee, K., and Reynolds, J. 'Tracing Decisions in the NHS', King's Fund Publication RC16 (1981).

Baumol, W. J. The Firm and its Objectives, 'Economic Theory and Operations Analysis' (Prentice-Hall, Englewood Cliffs, New Jersey, 1972).

Belson, W. Social Surveys: Pitfalls and Potential, 'Journal of the Royal Society of Arts' (May 1977).

Benson, J. K. The Interorganisational Network as a Political Economy, 'Administrative Science Quarterly', no. 20 (1975).

Berki, S. E. 'Hospital Economics' (Lexington Books and D. C. Heath, Lexington, Massachusetts, 1972).

Berry, D. E. The Transfer of Planning Theories to Health Planning Practice, 'Policy Sciences', no. 5 (1974).

Bice, T. Health Services Planning and Regulation in S. J. Williams and P. R. Torrens (eds.), 'Introduction to Health Services' (John Wiley, New York, 1980).

Birch, A. H. 'Representative and Responsible Government' (Allen and Unwin, London, 1964).

Blum, H. L. Review of 'Approaches to National Health Planning' by H. E. Hilliboe, A. Barkhuus and W. C. Thomas Jr., 'Public Health Paper No. 46 (WHO, Geneva, 1972)', 'International Journal of Health Services', vol. 4, no. 2 (1974).

Bochel, D., and MacLaren, M. Representing the Interests of the Public: the Case of the Local Health Council in Scotland, 'Journal of Social Policy', vol. 8, no. 4 (1979).

Booth, T. A. (ed.) 'Planning for Welfare: Social Policy and the Expenditure Process' (Basil Blackwell and Martin Robertson, Oxford, 1979).

--, Collaboration between the Health and Social Services: a Case Study of Joint Planning, 'Policy and Politics', vol. 9, no. 1 (1981).

Bourne, R. Joint Social Policy - Or Crowns and Courtiers, 'New Society', 27 November 1975.

Lord Boyle of Handsworth, Ministers and the Administrative Process, 'Public Administration', vol. 58 (Spring 1980).

Braybrooke, D., and Lindblom, C. E. 'A Strategy of Decision' (Free Press, New York, 1963).

Breton, A. Economics of Representative Democracy in IEA, 'The Economics of Politics' (IEA, London, 1979).

Brown, C. V., and Jackson, P. M. 'Public Sector Economics' (Martin Robertson, Oxford, 1978).

Brown, R. G. S. 'The Management of Welfare' (Fontana, London, 1975).

--, Accountability and Control in the NHS, 'Hospital and Health Services Review', Centre 8 Pages (1977).

--, 'Reorganising the NHS: a Case Study of Administrative Change' (Basil Blackwell and Martin Robertson, Oxford, 1979).

Buchanan, J. M. From Private Preferences to Public Philosophy, 'IEA Readings 18' (1978).

Burton, A. W., and Johnson, R. 'Public Participation in Planning: a Review of Experience in Scotland' (The Planning Exchange, Glasgow, 1976).

Caiden, N., and Wildavsky, A. 'Planning and Budgeting in Poor Countries' (John Wiley and Sons, New York, 1974).

Cang, S. Community Health Councils: Intentions, Problems and Possibilities in E. Jacques (ed.), 'Health Services: their Nature and Organisation, and the Role of Patients, Doctors and the Health Professions' (Brunel Health Services Organisation Research Unit, 1978).

Carley, M. 'Rational Techniques in Policy Analysis' (Heinemann, London, 1980).

Central Policy Review Staff, 'A Joint Framework for Social Policy' (HMSO, London, 1975).

--, 'Relations between Central Government and Local Authorities' (HMSO, London, 1976).

--, 'Population and Social Services' (HMSO, London, 1977).

Clarkson, K. Some Implications of Property Rights in Hospital Management, 'Journal of Law and Economics' (October 1972).

Craven, E. (ed.) 'Regional Devolution and Social Policy' (Macmillan Press, London, 1975).

Crossman, R. H. S. 'A Politician's View of Health Service Planning' (The University of Glasgow, Glasgow, 1972).

--, 'The Diaries of a Cabinet Minister, Volume 1, Minister of Housing 1964-66' (Hamish Hamilton and Jonathan Cape, London, 1975).

Culyer, A. J., Lavers, R., and Williams, A. Social Indicators: Health, 'Social Trends', no. 2 (1971).

Cyert, R. M., and March, J. G. 'A Behavioural Theory of the Firm' (Prentice-Hall, Englewood Cliffs, New Jersey, 1963).

Davies, J. G. 'The Evangelistic Bureaucrat: a Study of a Planning Exercise in Newcastle-upon-Tyne' (Tavistock Publications, London, 1972).

Dennis, N. 'Public Participation and Planners' Blight' (Faber, London, 1972).

Devine, P. J. et al. 'An Introduction to Industrial Economics' (Allen and Unwin, London, 1977).

DHSS 'Management Arrangements for the Reorganised National Health Service' (HMSO, London, 1972).

--, 'A Report from the Working Party on Collaboration between the NHS and Local Government on its Activities to the End of 1972' (HMSO, London, 1973).

--, 'The NHS Planning System' (HMSO, London, 1976).

--, 'Prevention and Health, Everybody's Business' (HMSO, London, 1976).

--, 'Priorities for the Health and Personal Social Services'

(HMSO, London, 1976).

--, 'Priorities in the Health and Personal Social Services: the Way Forward' (HMSO, London, 1977).

--, 'Inequalities in Health' (HMSO, London, 1980).

--, 'Patients First' (HMSO, London, 1980).

Dimmock, S. J. Participation or Control? The Workers' Involvement in Management in K. Barnard and K. Lee (eds.), 'Conflicts in the NHS' (Croom Helm, London, 1977).

Downs, A. 'An Economic Theory of Democracy' (Harper and Row, New York, 1957).

Doyal, L., and Pennell, I. 'The Political Economy of Health' (Pluto Press, London, 1979).

Draper, P. Value Judgements in Health Planning, 'Community Medicine' (February 1973).

--, 'Economic Policy and Health' (Unit for the Study of Health Policy, 1976).

Drummond, M. F. 'Principles of Economic Appraisal in Health Care' (Oxford University Press, Oxford, 1980).

Eckstein, H. 'Pressure Group Politics' (Allen and Unwin, London, 1960).

Etzioni, A. Mixed Scanning: a 'Third' Approach to Decision-Making, 'Public Administration Review' (December 1967).

Expenditure Committee (Employment and Social Services Sub-Committee), 1970-71 'Minutes of Evidence', HC323ii (HMSO, London, 31 March 1971).

Fagence, M. 'Citizen Participation in Planning' (Pergamon Press, Oxford, 1977).

Faludi, A. 'Planning Theory' (Pergamon Press, Oxford, 1973).

--, (ed.) 'A Reader in Planning Theory' (Pergamon Press, Oxford, 1973).

Feldstein, M. 'Economic Analysis for Health Service Efficiency' (North Holland Publishing Company, Amsterdam, 1967).

Feldstein, P. J. 'Health Care Economics' (John Wiley and Sons, New York, 1979).

Foltz, A.-M., Chen, M., and Stoga, A. Public Policy and Health Resource Distribution, 'Policy Sciences', vol. 8 (1977).

Forester, J. Critical Theory and Planning Practice, 'American Planning Association Journal' (July 1980).

Frieden, B. J., and Peters, J. Urban Planning and Health Services: Opportunities for Co-operation, 'Journal of the American Institute of Planners', vol. 36, no. 2 (1970).

Friedmann, J., A Conceptual Model for the Analysis of Planning Behaviour, 'Administrative Science Quarterly' (1967).

Friend, J. K., and Jessop, W. N. 'Local Government and Strategic Choice: an Operational Research Approach to the Processes of Public Planning' (Pergamon Press, Oxford, 1967).

--, Power, J. M., and Yewlett, C. J. L. 'Public Planning: the

Inter-Corporate Dimension' (Tavistock Publications, London, 1974).

Glennerster, H. Prime Cuts: Public Expenditure and Social Services Planning in a Hostile Environment, 'Policy and Politics', vol. 8, no. 4 (1980).

--, From Containment to Conflict? - Social Planning in the Seventies, 'Journal of Social Policy', vol. 10, no. 1 (1981).

Gordon, I., Lewis, J., and Young, K. Perspectives on Policy Analysis, 'Public Administration Bulletin', no. 25 (1977).

Gray, A. M., and Steele, R. Beyond the Programme Budget, Economics and Resource Planning in the NHS, 'Hospital and Health Services Review' (March, 1980).

Griffith, J. A. G. 'Central Departments and Local Authorities' (Allen and Unwin, London, 1966).

Grosse, R. N. Problems of Resource Allocation in Health in R. H. Haveman and J. Margolis (eds.), 'Public Expenditure and Policy Analysis' (Markham Publishing Company, Chicago, 1970).

--, Cost Benefit Analysis in Disease Control Programs in M. G. Kendall (ed.), 'Cost Benefit Analysis' (English Universities Press, London, 1971).

Hall, P., Land, H., Parker, R., and Webb, A. 'Change, Choice and Conflict in Social Policy' (Heinemann, London, 1975).

Ham, C. J. Power, Patients and Pluralism in K. Barnard and K. Lee (eds.), 'Conflicts in the NHS' (Croom Helm, London, 1977).

--, Approaches to the Study of Social Policy Making, 'Policy and Politics', vol. 8, no. 1 (1980).

--, Community Health Council Participation in the NHS Planning System, 'Social Policy and Administration', vol. 14, no. 3 (Autumn 1980).

--, 'Policy Making in the NHS' (Macmillan, London, 1981).

Harris, G., and Parker C. Exploring the Twisting Road to and from the Staging Post, 'Health and Social Service Journal', 14 December 1979.

Harris, J. E. The Internal Organisation of Hospitals: Some Economic Implications, 'The Bell Journal of Economics', vol. 8, no. 2 (Autumn 1977).

Harrison, S. The Politics of Health Manpower in A. Long and G. Mercer (eds.), 'Manpower Planning in the NHS' (Gower Press, Farnborough, 1981).

Haveman, R. H. Policy Analysis and the Congress: an Economist's View, 'Policy Analysis', vol. 2, no. 2 (Spring 1976).

--, and Margolis, J. (eds.), 'Public Expenditure and Policy Analysis', 2nd edn (Rand McNally College Publishing Company, Chicago, 1977).

Hay, D. A., and Morris, D. J. 'Industrial Economics: Theory and Practice' (Oxford University Press, Oxford, 1979).

Haywood, S., and Alaszewski, A. 'Crisis in the Health

Service: the Politics of Management' (Croom Helm, London, 1980).

Healey, P. Networking as a Normative Principle, with Particular Reference to Local Government and Land Use Planning, 'Local Government Studies', vol. 5, no. 1 (1979).

Heclo, H., and Wildavsky, A. 'The Private Government of Public Money' (Macmillan, London, 1974).

Higgins, J. The Unfulfilled Promise of Policy Research, 'Social Policy and Administration', vol. 14, no. 3 (Autumn 1980).

Hirsch, W. Z. Program Budgeting in the UK, 'Public Administration Review' (March/April 1973).

House of Commons Expenditure Committee 'Policy-Making in the Department of Education and Science', Tenth Report from the Expenditure Committee, Sessions 1975-6 (1976).

Illich, I. 'Medical Nemesis: the Expropriation of Health' (Calder and Boyars, London, 1975),

Jacobs, P. A Survey of Economic Models of Hospitals, 'Inquiry' (June 1974).

Judge, K. 'Rationing Social Services: a Study of Resource Allocation and the Personal Social Services' (Heinemann, London, 1978).

Kellner, P., and Lord Crowther-Hunt 'The Civil Servants: an Inquiry into Britain's Ruling Class' (Macdonald, London, 1980).

Killick, T., and Kinyua, J. K. On Implementing Development Plans: a Case Study, 'ODI Review', no. 1 (1980).

Klein, R. Accountability in the NHS, 'Political Quarterly', vol. 42, no. 4 (1971).

--, Policy-Making in the National Health Service, 'Political Studies', vol. XXII, no. 1 (1974).

--, Policy Problems and Policy Perceptions in the National Health Service, 'Policy and Politics', vol. 2, no. 3 (1974).

--, and Lewis, J. 'The Politics of Consumer Representation' (Centre for Studies in Social Policy, 1976).

--, The Rise and Decline of Policy Analysis: the Strange Case of Health Policymaking in Britain, 'Policy Analysis', vol. 2, no. 3 (Summer 1976).

--, The Corporate State, the Health Service and the Professions, 'New Universities Quarterly', vol. 31, no. 2(1977).

--, Priorities and the Problems of Planning, 'British Medical Journal', 22 October 1977.

--, The Strategy Behind the Jenkin Non-Strategy, 'British Medical Journal', 28 March 1981.

Krause, E. A. Health Planning as a Managerial Ideology, 'International Journal of Health Services', vol. 3, no. 3 (1973).

Lalonde, M. 'A New Perspective on the Health of Canadians' (Government of Canada, Ottawa, 1974).

Layfield, F. 'Local Government Finance', Report of the Committee of Enquiry (HMSO, London, 1976).

Lee, K. Public Expenditure, Planning and Local Democracy in K. Barnard and K. Lee (eds.), 'Conflicts in the National Health Service' (Croom Helm, London, and Prodist, New York, 1977).

--, and Mills, A. The Contribution of Economics to Health Service Planning: a Review of the State of the Art, 'Health and Social Services Journal' (February 1979).

--, Health Care: Planning, Policies and Incentives, 'Futures', vol. 11, no. 6 (1979).

--, Need Versus Demand: the Planner's Dilemma in K. Lee (ed.), 'Economics and Health Planning' (Croom Helm, London, and Health Administration Press, Ann Arbor, 1979).

--, Political Economy of Health Care in England in G. I. Misek (ed.), 'Socioeconomic Issues of Health 1979' (American Medical Association, Chicago, Illinois, 1979).

--, and Mills, A. The Role of Economists and Economics in Health Service Planning: a General Overview in K. Lee (ed.), 'Economics and Health Planning' (Croom Helm, London, and Health Administration Press, Ann Arbor, 1979).

--, Public Expenditure, Health Services, and Health, in A. Walker (ed.), 'Public Expenditure and Social Priorities' (Heinemann, London, 1981).

Lee, M. L. A Conspicuous Production Theory of Hospital Behaviour, 'Southern Economic Journal', vol. 31, no. 1 (July 1971).

Levin, A. L. Cost Effectiveness in Maternal and Child Health, 'New England Journal of Medicine', 9 May 1968.

Levin, P. Opening Up the Planning Process in S. Hatch (ed.), 'Towards Participation in Local Services', Fabian Tract 419 (1973).

Lewis, S. Weaving a Stratagem across Boundaries, 'Health and Social Service Journal', 6 April 1979.

Leys, C. The Analysis of Planning in C. Leys (ed.), 'Politics and Change in Developing Countries' (Cambridge University Press, Cambridge, 1969).

Lind, G., and Wiseman, C. Setting Health Priorities: a Review of Concepts and Approaches, 'Journal of Social Policy', vol. 7, no. 4 (1978).

Lindblom, C. E. The Science of 'Muddling Through', 'Public Administration Review' (Spring 1959).

--, 'The Limits of Democracy' (Free Press, New York, 1964).

--, Still Muddling, Not Yet Through, 'Public Administration Review' (November/December 1979).

Lindsay, C. M., et al. 'National Health Issues: the British Experience' (Roche Laboratories, Welwyn Garden, March 1980).

Litsios, S. The Principles and Methods of Evaluation of National Health Plans, 'International Journal of Health Services', vol. 4, no. 2 (1971).

Lukes, S. 'Power, a Radical View' (Macmillan, London, 1974).
Mackenzie, W. J. M. 'Power and Responsibility in Health Care' (Oxford University Press, Oxford, 1979).
Maddox, G. L. Muddling Through: Planning for Health Care in England, 'Medical Care', vol. IX, no. 5 (1972).
Mahler, H. Health for All by the Year 2000, 'World Health' (February/March 1981).
Manor, Y., and Sheffer, G. Can Planning be Salvaged?, 'Public Administration', vol. 55 (Summer 1977).
Marmor, T. R., and Bridges, A. American Health Planning and the Lessons of Comparative Policy Analysis, 'Journal of Health Politics, Policy and Law', vol. 5, no. 3 (1980).
Marris, P., and Rein, M. 'Dilemmas of Social Reform' (Routledge and Kegan Paul, London, 1967).
Marris, R. 'Economic Theory of Managerial Capitalism' (Macmillan, London, 1964).
McKinlay, J. B. Epidemiological and Political Determinants of Social Policies Regarding the Public Health, 'Social Science and Medicine', vol. 13A (1979).
Mechanic, D. The Growth of Medical Technology and Bureaucracy: Implications for Medical Care, 'Milbank Memorial Fund Quarterly' (Winter 1977).
Mersey Regional Health Authority, 'Report of the Liverpool Committee of Inquiry' (1978).
Migue, J. L., and Belanger, G. Towards a Theory of Managerial Discretion, 'Public Choice' (Spring 1974).
Mills, A. J., and Reynolds, J. Centre-Periphery: Can Guidelines Bridge the Gap?, 'Hospital and Health Services Review' (February 1977).
Mooney, G. H. 'The Valuation of Human Life' (Macmillan, London, 1977).
--, Planning for Balance of Care of the Elderly, 'Scottish Journal of Political Economy' (June 1978).
--, 'Choices for Health Care' (Macmillan, London, 1980).
Newhouse, J. P. Toward a Theory of Nonprofit Institutions: an Economic Model of a Hospital, 'The American Economic Review' (March 1970).
Niskanen, W. A. 'Bureaucracy and Representative Government' (Aldine Press, Chicago, 1971).
--, Competition among Government Bureaus, 'IEA Readings 18' (1979).
Noad, A., and King, L. Area Co-ordination: Some Experiences Compared, 'Linkage Two' (1977).
Novick, D. (ed.) 'Program Budgeting, Program Analysis and the Federal Budget' (Rand Corporation, 1965).
OECD 'Social Change in OECD Countries 1950-1980' (OECD Observer, No. 107, 1980).
Parston, G. 'Planners, Politics and Health Services' (Croom Helm, London, 1980).
Pateman, C. 'Participation and Democratic Theory' (Cambridge University Press, Cambridge, 1970).

Bibliography

Pauly, M., and Redisch, M. The Not-for-Profit Hospital as a Physicians' Co-operative, 'The American Economic Review' (March 1973).

Peacock, A. The Economics of Bureaucracy: an Inside View, in IEA, 'The Economics of Politics' (IEA, London, 1979).

Phillips, D. The Creation of Consultative Councils in the NHS, 'Public Administration', vol. 58 (Spring 1980).

Pole, J. D. Programmes, Priorities and Budgets, 'British Journal of Preventive and Social Medicine', vol. 28 (1974).

Powell, J. E. 'Medicine and Politics: 1975 and After' (Pitman Medical, Tunbridge Wells, 1976).

Radical Statistics Health Group 'Whose Priorities?' (1977).

Razzell, E. J. Planning in Whitehall - Is it Possible? - Will it Survive?, 'Long Range Planning', vol. 13 (February 1980).

Rhodes, R. A. W. Research into Central-Local Relations in Britain: a Framework for Analysis in SSRC, 'Central-Local Government Relationships' (Social Science Research Council, London, 1979).

Richards, K. 'The NHS and Social Services', King's Fund Project Paper No. RC11 (1980).

Rickard, J. H. Per Capita Expenditure of the English Area Health Authorities, 'British Medical Journal', 31 January 1976.

Rivlin, A. M. The Planning Programming Budgeting System in Health, Education and Welfare: Some Lessons from Experience in R. H. Haveman and J. Margolis (eds.), 'Public Expenditure and Policy Analysis' (Markham Publishing Company, Chicago, 1970).

Royal Commission on the NHS, 'Management of Financial Resources in the NHS', Research Paper No. 2 (HMSO, London, 1978).

Salmon, J. W., and Berliner, H. S. Health Policy Implications of the Holistic Health Movement, 'Journal of Health Politics, Policy and Law', vol. 5, no. 3 (Fall 1980).

Sargeant, T. Joint Care Planning in the Health and Personal Social Services in T. A. Booth (ed.), 'Planning for Welfare: Social Policy and the Expenditure Process' (Basil Blackwell and Martin Robertson, Oxford, 1979).

SAUS, Implementation and the Central-Local Relationship in SSRC, 'Central-Local Government Relationships' (Social Science Research Council, London, 1979).

Sawyer, M. C. 'Theories of the Firm' (Weidenfeld and Nicolson, London, 1979).

Schick, A. The Road to PPB in F. J. Lyden and E. G. Miller (eds.), 'Planning, Programming, Budgeting' (Chicago, 1972).

--, A Death in the Bureaucracy: the Demise of Federal PPB, 'Public Administration Review' (March/April 1973).

Schon, D. 'Beyond the Stable State' (Temple Smith, London, 1971).

Self, P. 'Administrative Theories and Politics' (George Allen and Unwin, London, 1974).

Shani, M. Futures Studies Versus Planning, 'Omega', vol. 2, no. 5 (1974).

Shaw, S. H. A. The Pleasures and Perils of Joint Care Planning, 'Royal Society of Health Journal', vol. 98, no. 4 (1978).

Simon, H. A. 'Administrative Behaviour' (Macmillan, London, 1957).

Skeffington Report 'People and Planning' (HMSO, London, 1969).

SSRC 'Central-Local Government Relationships' (Social Science Research Council, London, 1979).

Stanyer, J. 'Understanding Local Government' (Fontana, London, 1976).

Stoller, E. P. New Roles for Health Care Consumers: a Study of Role Transformation, 'Journal of Community Health', vol. 3, no. 2 (1977).

Storey, D. J. The Economics of Bureaux: the Case of London Boroughs 1970-76, 'Applied Economics' (June 1980).

Straw, J. 'Power in Government - a Chinese Puzzle', Convocation Lecture, Leeds University, 1978.

Sudama, T. PPBS and Theories of Decision-Making, Bureaucracy and Politics, 'Public Finance', vol. 32, no. 3 (1977).

Tannen, L. Health Planning as a Regulatory Strategy: a Discussion of its History and Current Uses, 'International Journal of Health Services', vol. 10, no. 1 (1980).

Taylor, R. The Local Health System: an Ethnography of Interest Groups and Decision-Making, 'Social Science and Medicine', vol. 11 (1977).

--, The Local Health System: Observations on the Exercise of Professional Influence, 'Health and Social Service Journal', Centre Eight Papers (1977).

Towell, D. Giving Fresh Impetus to Collaboration, 'Health and Social Service Journal' (July 1981).

Tullock, G. Bureaucracy and the Growth of Government, 'IEA Readings 21' (IEA, London, 1979).

Turner, J. No Votes, No Hopes, 'New Society', 26 April 1979.

Warner, K. E., and Hutton, R. C. Cost-Benefit and Cost-Effectiveness Analysis in Health Care, 'Medical Care', vol. XVIII, no. 11 (1980).

Waterston, A. An Operational Approach to Development Planning, 'International Journal of Health Services', no. 3 (1971).

WHO, 'Primary Health Care', (WHO, Geneva, 1978).

--, 'Formulating Strategies for Health for All by the Year 2000', (WHO, Geneva, 1979).

--, 'Guiding Principles for the Managerial Process for National Health Development' (WHO, Geneva, September 1980).

Wildavsky, A. 'The Politics of the Budgeting Process' (Little, Brown and Company, Boston, 1964).

--, Rescuing Policy Analysis from PPBS, 'Public Administration Review' (March/April 1969).

--, Doing Better and Feeling Worse: the Political Pathology of Health Policy in J. H. Knowles (ed.), 'Doing Better and Feeling Worse: Health in the United States' (Norton, New York, 1977).

Williamson, O. E. 'The Economics of Discretionary Behaviour' (Prentice-Hall, Englewood Cliffs, New Jersey, 1963).

Wiseman, C. 'Strategic Planning in the Scottish Health Service - a Mixed-Scanning Approach' (Tavistock Insitute of Human Relations, London, June 1977).

--, Selection of Major Planning Issues, 'Policy Sciences', vol. 9 (1978).

Wistow, G., and Webb, A. 'Patients First, One Step Backwards for Collaboration' (Loughborough University, Loughborough, 1981).

World Bank 'Health: Sector Policy Paper', 2nd edn (World Bank, Washington, DC, February 1980).